FOLK TALES OF THE HIGHLANDS

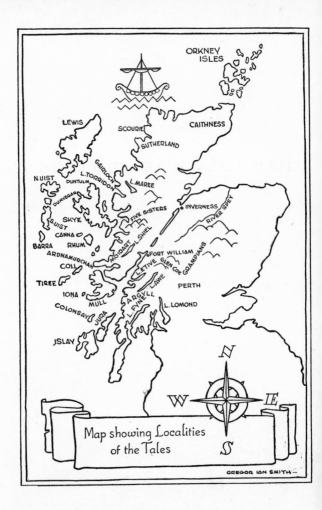

Map showing Localities
of the Tales

GREGOR IAN SMITH

FOLK TALES OF THE HIGHLANDS

GREGOR IAN SMITH

Drawings by the Author

THOMAS NELSON AND SONS LTD
LONDON AND EDINBURGH

THOMAS NELSON AND SONS LTD

Parkside Works Edinburgh 9
3 Henrietta Street London WC2
312 Flinders Street Melbourne C1
5 Parker's Buildings Burg Street Cape Town

THOMAS NELSON AND SONS (CANADA) LTD
91–93 Wellington Street West   Toronto 1

THOMAS NELSON AND SONS
19 East 47th Street New York 17

SOCIÉTÉ FRANÇAISE D'EDITIONS NELSON
25 rue Henri Barbusse Paris Ve

First published April 1953
Reprinted 1954

CONTENTS

v

CONTENTS

FOR KIRSTEEN MARY

ACKNOWLEDGMENT

The author is greatly indebted to Alexander Nicolson for permission to include the poems 'Cronan a' chait,' and 'Songs of the Birds' from *Oideas na Cloinne*.

1 THE LITTLE BANNOCK

MORAG, the wife of Donald the crofter at Duntulm, was easily the laziest woman in the island of Skye. She had little to complain of, for Donald's house was small and easily managed, the drinking-well was not a step from the door, and neither child nor dog was there to be dirtying the place. Donald, a patient man, saw to it that peats were always piled at the gable ready for the fire. He it was who tended the two cows, and grew the finest crops in that far corner of Skye. Yet Morag complained and lamented, idling away her time, until Donald was hard put to it to keep from beating her with the porridge-spoon.

One morning she looked round the untidy kitchen. The ashes strewed the hearth, the bed was still to be made, the dishes were unwashed. Even the spinning-wheel was white with dust and cobwebs.

' Dear, oh dear ! ' she whimpered as she stirred the porridge in the pot. ' It seems that I must work and work and work all my life. And there is nothing I can think of that is more unpleasant ! ' She thought so much about it that she forgot to keep stirring ; the porridge became lumpy and stuck to the bottom of the pot, which made Morag more discontented than ever. And then, quite suddenly, she remembered that sometimes the fairies could be persuaded to come and work for human beings. And was there not a fairy hill at the back of the house, or so it was said !

The lazy woman decided that there would be no harm in asking their help, so she poured the porridge into a bowl, mixed it with cream and set it outside on the step. No fairy, she knew, could resist a bowl of porridge and cream. Indeed there was no better way to tempt the wee folk. So she hid behind the door and waited.

Morag had not long to wait. There was a sudden scurrying and scuffling of feet on the path. The horn spoon began to click against the porridge-bowl. Morag peeped out to see what was happening. Sure enough there they were, a score of them, gathered round the dish, taking turns to sup. Not one of the little people was more than a span high, each was dressed in green and their movements were like the scurrying of mice.

To be sure the porridge disappeared quickly. As soon as it was finished the fairies began to bang on the door until Morag was glad to let them in. 'Good morning,' she greeted her visitors, 'I am hoping it is work you seek.'

'Aye and so, wife,' they replied. 'Work we will, but eat we must. So fetch your girdle, mistress, and toast your bannocks. For it is hungry we will be before the day is out.'

Morag fetched the girdle and began to bake oat bannocks, while the fairies went hustling and bustling about the house, as busy as ants. Some swept the floors, some drew down the cobwebs, some hurried to make butter, some busied themselves weaving, while others carded, pulled and teased the wool, until the spinning-wheel was humming merrily. Never in that house had there been so much mending and patching and scrubbing and cleaning!

Meanwhile Morag was busy baking bannocks, until they began to pile up on the kitchen table. But scarcely had they cooled than the fairies stopped their work and ate them up to the very last crumb. This happened so often that Morag was in despair. But she did not dare to complain, for fear of being

2

3

bewitched or carried off to the fairy hill. And so she baked and kneaded and turned her girdle until the last crumb of oatmeal was finished.

Then there was a fine to-do. They clamoured for bannocks until Morag was obliged to go in search of more meal from a neighbour. She ran as fast as she could to the village where she sought the house of the oldest woman.

' What am I to do ? ' cried the wretched Morag bitterly. ' My husband has gone to the shieling, my kitchen is full of fairies and they are eating us out of house and home ! Tell me what I must do to be rid of them, Grandmother ! '

' Tell me first how they found their way across the threshold,' asked the *cailleach*.[1] Morag confessed at last how she had tempted the fairies with a bowl of porridge and cream, so that they would work for her.

' Then let this be a lesson to you, Morag of the white hands, never to trust the wee folk, and never to give way to laziness. Now be off home with you, and when you reach the door open it and cry, " Run, run ! Your house is on fire ! " The fairies will run back to the hill. But when they find they have been deceived they will return to your kitchen and carry you off with them.'

' Oh dear,' wailed Morag, wringing her hands. ' Is there nothing I can do to keep them outside ? I have no wish to live inside the fairy hill for the rest of my life ! '

' Whenever you enter the house see to it that you upset each thing that the fairies have been using, or else the door that you lock and bolt will be opened for them.'

Morag thanked the old woman, hurried home, and when she reached the cottage she tiptoed to the door

[1] *cailleach*, old woman

4

and listened. The fairies were all busy. She opened the door a little, popped her head in and cried, ' Run, run ! Your house is on fire ! ' Immediately the fairies stopped their work and came tumbling out of the door, running as fast as their little legs would take them to the fairy hill. Morag skipped inside and locked and barred the door.

Then she went round the house turning everything topsy-turvy. When she had finished she almost wept at the dreadful disorder, for the fairies had left everything in place. But she had little time to survey her handiwork, for the fairies were back again in the twinkling of an eye, screaming outside the door, demanding to be let in again.

' Open the door to us, housewife ! ' they clamoured through the keyhole.

' I cannot leave the girdle ! ' replied Morag. ' My bannocks would burn.'

' Open the door, brush that stands by the fire ! '

' I cannot for I am standing on my head,' replied the brush.

' Open the door to us, spinning-wheel ! '

' I cannot, for my wheel is tied,' replied the spinning-wheel.

Thus did the pots, the pans, the platters, indeed everything that was in the kitchen, reply to the angry fairies, until at length they appealed to a little bannock that had rolled into a dark corner. ' Open the door, little bannock ! ' they squeaked in their shrill voices, and immediately the little bannock began to roll across the floor.

It skipped across Morag's toes, ran round the table, and would have reached the door had not she leapt over a chair and crushed it to crumbs under her foot. At that very moment she heard her husband's voice outside on the hill. The spell was broken. With a noise like the wind in the chimney the fairies ran off, never to return.

Morag was careful after that never to mention the fairies by name. From that day she gave up her lazy habits and became a good wife to Donald the crofter. But her husband had always great difficulty in persuading her to bake bannocks, which, I am sure you agree, was not surprising!

2 A HIGHLAND SAMSON

THE Highlands of Scotland have bred many strong men, and one of them was Alasdair Cameron of Lochaber. One day Cameron was going home when he overtook a neighbour whose horse and cart had foundered in a ditch. He immediately went to his friend's assistance. The horse was persuaded to try and shift the tilted cart but the animal was too exhausted and went down on its knees. Cameron decided to get the beast out of the shafts. He removed the harness and heaved the horse out of the way. Then he took its place between the shafts, braced his shoulders and dragged the cart from the ditch back to the road again.

' There you are, Murdoch,' he said. ' But I am not surprised the horse could not pull it out. I was hard put to it to do it myself.'

3 CRONAN A' CHAIT

Falbhan na h-oidhche,
Falbhan na h-oidhche,
Falbhan na h-oidhche, ars an cat glas.
Falbhan na h-oidhche gun solus gun soillse,
Falbhan na h-oidhche, ars an cat glas.
Obair a thogadh mo chridhe le aoibhneas,
Falbhan na h-oidhche, ars an cat glas.
A sealg am onar am frogaibh nan saibhlean,
Falbhan na h-oidhche, ars an cat glas.
Na luchain bheag ghionach
Tha fuireach 's an aite,
Bha riamh ris a' chriomadh
'S a milleadh na dh' fhag iad,
Fhad 's a mhaireas na dubhain
Tha falaicht am spagan
Theid ruaig air a' ghraisg ud
Chun nam blaran a muigh.
Seo an siaghdear gun ghiorag,
An gille neo-sgathach,
Fear faire na h-oidhche,
A chlaoidheas gach meirleach
'S a smadas gach luch,
Falbhan na h-oidhche,
Falbhan na h-oidhche,
Falbhan na h-oidhche, ars an cat glas.

THE PURRING OF THE CAT

Prowling by night,
Prowling by night,
Prowling by night, quoth the grey cat.
Prowling at night without a chink of light,
Prowling at night, quoth the grey cat.
Hunting alone in the nooks of the barns,
Prowling at night, quoth the grey cat.
Work to lift my heart with delight,
Prowling by night, quoth the grey cat.
The little greedy mice
That haunt the place,
Ever a-nibbling
And spoiling the leavings,
So long as will last the claws
That are concealed in my paws
That rabble will be routed
To the fields outside.
Here's the soldier without fear,
The lad without panic,
The watchman of the night
Who will harass all thieves
And subdue all mice,
Prowling by night,
Prowling by night,
Prowling by night, quoth the grey cat.

4 KING SALMON

THE king of all salmon lived by himself in the deepest
pool of the Orchy. It was a lonely pool, hidden under
the shadow of a mighty rock, and veiled by rowan-
trees. No-one knew the great salmon lived there but
Gobha Dubh, the little dipper who could walk under
water, and *Clamhan*, the keen-eyed buzzard who
hunted the hillside. But one day Tormod the hermit
found where the salmon had hidden himself. His
aged hands shook as he leaned to watch the moving
shape in the depths beneath, for he knew there was
no-one in this world as wise as King Salmon.

Each day as the old man came to watch the fish in
secret his mind was busy with but one thought—how
to catch the monster and eat his flesh. For if he
could eat of its flesh then the wisdom of the salmon
would be his.

Tormod himself was old and frail. Certainly he
was no match for so mighty a creature. Who then
must be found to make the catch ? Tormod considered the problem for many days, and then he knew.
Who indeed but the lithe young giant Laochan who
had more strength and courage than any hunter in
the land ! Laochan would kill the fish and cook the
flesh, but he must not be allowed to eat. For by
eating, Laochan and not Tormod the hermit would
inherit the worldly wisdom that lay in the heart of
the great fish.

Laochan listened to the words of the hermit. ' I
have a task for you,' said Tormod. ' A task that
will test your manhood.' And, as the young man
listened, Tormod told him of the lordly salmon lying
in the depths of the pool. ' Catch the fish,' added the
cunning Tormod, ' and cook him for me to eat and

I will spread the word of your skill and greatness across the land. I am an old man, and before my time comes to die I have a yearning to eat of salmon. And who better than you to take so mighty a fish from its fastness, to please a foolish old man!'

Laochan smiled as the old man pleaded his wish. ' But,' continued the hermit, ' see to it that no crumb of the beast's flesh touches your lips for it has the power to wither the tongue and bring death to the taster.'

' Indeed!' replied Laochan in surprise. ' How then will you eat of the poisoned salmon, Tormod?'

' I have a magic salve to sweeten the dish and destroy its evil powers. Then when I have tasted we may sit and eat together. Come, Laochan, kill the fish and please an old man.'

' I will try my skill, Tormod,' replied young Laochan, and went off leaving the hermit well pleased with his plans.

By the light of the moon Laochan lay by the rock pool. He let the moon strike full upon his burnished targe so that the double beam flashed upon the water. Presently the surface stirred. The head of the great salmon could be seen rising to the light. Laochan poised his spear and struck. At once the pool, crimson with the creature's blood, surged and boiled as the salmon lashed its tail in fury. All night the struggle went on, but with the coming of dawn the salmon's strength was spent. Laochan rose wearily and bearing the dead salmon on his back went to prepare the feast.

As Laochan set the cauldron to boil upon a great fire, Tormod came to watch. He said no word as the fish was cleaned and laid within the pot, but his eyes were bright with greed and anticipation of the wisdom that would soon be his when the feast was ready. Meanwhile Laochan was careful that no flesh touched his lips lest his life be forfeit. But he was so weary that his hand was unsteady. As he removed the fish he touched the rim of the pot, and scorched his fingers. At once he sucked the hurt and a crumb of salmon lay on his tongue.

Tormod the hermit, seeing this, raised his skinny arms and cried out in anguish. Laochan had eaten first, and having eaten had inherited the salmon's wisdom! And so it was, for if the tales be true Laochan in his lifetime proved himself as wise and great as Solomon himself. But Tormod died a lonely and miserable old man in his cell by the rock pool.

PISEAG BHEAG, PISEAG BHEAG
(*Pussy cat, pussy cat*)

' Phiseag bheag, phiseag bheag,
Cait an robh thusa ? '
' Ag ceilidh air a' bhan-righ
Shios am baile Lunnainn.'
' Phiseag bheag, phiseag bheag,
Gu de rinn thus' an siud ? '
' Fo chathair mhoir na Ban-righ
Air m'onair ghlac mi luch.'

*

Airde na daileach is isle na h-airde.
The highest part of the meadow and the lowest sides of
the ridges (the best of arable land).

5 THE GIANTS OF LOCH SHIEL

IF you were to walk inland from the shores of Loch
Shiel you would come upon a little green glen hidden
between the folds of blue mountains. You might be
struck by the level fields and the smoothness of the
slopes, and wonder why this should be so when in the
neighbourhood the glens are rough and strewn everywhere with grey rocks.

Many years ago the little glen was a bleak barren
place too, with boulders blocking every path, and
heaps of jagged stones and rocks on every hand. The
people living in the glen were poor, for there was little
soil where crops would grow, and only the poorest
pastures to feed their lean cattle.

Half-way down the glen there lived a *seanchaidh* [1]
in a small black house hidden against the hillside.
Besides being a wonderful story-teller the old man

[1] *seanchaidh*, story-teller

12

was very wise. One day the young men came to him.
' We are the poorest of our race,' they said, ' because
our glen is small and mean, and choked with great
splinters of rock fallen from the mountains. Our
crops seldom ripen to the full ear, and our cattle are
easily stolen by thieves who hide amongst the wilder-
ness of stones. Is there no place where we can live,
where the hills are smooth and kindly, and the straths
are easily tilled ? '

In answer the *seanchaidh* rolled aside the stones
and loosened the earth. ' There is no finer soil than
in our glen,' he replied.

' That may be so,' replied the young men. ' But
to clear away the rocks would be a task even for the
gods, and we are only men.'

Now, at that time there were giants living in the
land. Two great surly creatures lived in the neighbouring mountains, and they were forever quarrelling
about their strength. That day the *seanchaidh*
climbed high into the mists and spoke to each in turn.
' It is a foolish thing to be forever quarrelling,' he said.
' I am but a poor old man, but it seems to me that
such a quarrel can be settled easily. Come down into
the glen where all the people can see your greatness.
And I will set you a task to prove your strength so that
it can be seen by all which of you is the mightier
giant.'

The next day there was a great rumbling on the
mountain-side and the two giants met in the glen.
The *seanchaidh* and all the people watched their
coming. ' Now let us see who can throw a small stone
to the mountain-top,' said the old man.

At that the giants laughed and each lifting a rock
as easily as a man would take a pebble from the shore,
they hurled them into the mountains, far out of sight.
' Indeed, and I have never seen stones fly so far

13

At their the given heading said city being a rank
and you as a wood which user a middle home of course
they should there take the despite, not not of while
behind with I down there some some the on the

14

before. But this time let the stones be bigger,' said the *seanchaidh*.

This time the giants lifted rocks seven times the size of a man's head and tossed them easily beyond the mountains. The people heard them rolling faintly into the corries, and they shook with fear.

'It's hard to choose who is the stronger,' said the *seanchaidh*. 'But there are many rocks in this place, and boulders bigger than our own houses. Let us see how many rocks each can throw first with his left hand, then with his right.'

The giants began immediately to hurl rocks far into the air and over the mountains with their left hands. On they went, striding the length of the glen, tearing boulders from the earth, and the noise that rose as the flying boulders sped westwards across the mountains was like the tempests of winter.

Presently they tired of throwing with their left hands. But they continued the contest by throwing with their right hands until the evening came. By then there was scarcely one rock to be seen anywhere. And the giants were so weary they could hardly stand.

'By the Seven Bright Stars,' said the *seanchaidh*, 'there is still no knowing who is the stronger, for we have lost count of what has been thrown. Go you now and look for the rock that has been thrown farthest. And when it has been found bring it to us, and we shall see who can repeat the feat. For only then can we know the mightier giant.'

Still quarrelling fiercely the stupid giants went off in search of the rock that had been thrown the farthest. And for all I know they are searching to this day, for they have never returned. But it is said that the noise of their quarrelling can still be heard when the wind is in the right place.

As for the people in the glen, they made haste to till the soil that the giants had uncovered. And today there are no finer crops growing anywhere than in the little green glen by Loch Shiel.

GU MARGADH, GU MARGADH
To market, to market

Gu margadh, gu margadh,
A cheannach uircean reamhar ;
Ob, ob, air an each,
Siud sinn a' dol dhachaidh.

Gu margadh, gu margadh,
A cheannach muc mhor ;
Ob, ob, air an each,
Dhachaidh leis air rop.

Gu margadh, gu margadh,
A cheannach aran-cridhe ;
'S cha teid sinn gu margadh
Gu 'm bi i ann a rithis.

6 THE PIPER'S CAVE

THERE are many tales, more than I care to remember, about pipers who set out to explore strange caves and were never heard of again. I shall tell you two such tales, the first about Alasdair Ban of Skye, a young man belonging to a great family of pipers called MacCrimmon.

One day Alasdair Ban was out on the hillside pulling bracken to be dried for winter bedding. As was his habit he had with him his pipes to practise when the work was done. But the sun in the cloudless sky soon made the work tedious, and the lad was glad to lay his cheek down on the soft undergrowth of moss and rest a while.

Presently he fell asleep, to dream of a quiet stream where a water-ouzel sat on a stone and sang to his own reflection. When he awoke the music was still in his ears. By his side lay his beloved pipes, tempting him to play the notes remembered from the dream. And he told himself he would work twice as hard once he had recaptured the melody.

No sooner had he begun to play than the wind ceased and a strangeness came upon the hillside. With a great crack it split open before his eyes, so that he was able to look deep down into a dark cave.

What boy can resist a cave! For all his sudden fear, this one tempted him strangely. The music, too, sounded sweeter in the hollow corridor, which echoed and twisted all his tunes. In he went boldly until he reached the first turn. A sudden darkening made him turn his head to see the doorway suddenly close and the sunlight disappear. This made him much afraid, and he made haste to find some way to escape. But the cave grew darker. He stumbled against the walls of black rock. Water dripped from overhead, and at last he had to sit down and rest.

He had not waited long before he heard little feet pattering in the gloom. A light appeared and all at once he saw a company of little men before him.

' You have been long in coming, Alasdair Ban,' they cried in their shrill small voices. ' But you are still welcome.'

They led him farther into the hollow hill, lighting his path with their lantern, until they reached a great hall filled with people. Lanterns and torches burned round the walls. A feast had been prepared before a golden throne on which a maiden sat in splendour. She was the most beautiful creature he had ever seen.

'Come, Alasdair Ban,' she cried in welcome. 'Sit with us at our feast. Then let us hear your music so that we may begin our dance.'

When the feasting was over, Alasdair began to play. In and out and round about skipped the little people on tireless feet. The lights burned low, his fingers ached, but there was no stopping. The spell that had been put upon him would not let him cease his piping.

Meantime in the world outside everyone was searching for the boy. They looked far into the glens and mountain ways, and across the wide moors, but save for the bracken he had left to dry above his own father's croft, there was no sign of the lad.

Sometimes they fancied they heard the strains of his piping borne on the wind; sometimes it seemed that the sound came from under their feet. And often his mother fancied she heard faint music under the flagstone on which the fire burned. But Alasdair Ban did not return, and she wept bitterly for her lost son.

How long Alasdair continued to play he had no means of knowing. But there came a time when he could play no longer. 'May God bless you, fairy queen,' he cried wearily, 'but I cannot play another note,' and he dropped in a swoon before the throne. Immediately the lights went out, and the fairy company disappeared. When Alasdair Ban raised his head again he found himself alone upon the windy hillside.

In the morning he reached the door of his own house. Trees had grown about the place; a wall stood where no wall had been before, and a bent old woman was drawing water at the well. She looked at the tall stranger who had come, and asked his name.

'Your own son, Mother,' he replied, putting his hand upon her shoulder, 'Alasdair Ban, who went to pull the bracken yesterday. A strange dream I have had, Mother, and glad I am to be home again. But what change is this I see in you, and upon this place, tell me ? '

The old woman found it hard to believe it was her son who had returned in the guise of a stranger with a beard on his face. But when she heard his strange tale of the fairies dancing to his music in the hollow of the hillside, she understood and wept for joy. Not one night but many she had waited for his return, until the days became months and ten long years had passed.

Alasdair lived to be an old man and a famous piper. But never again would he play the strange tune he had learned from the little black water-ouzel that sang to him in his dream upon the hillside.

7   THE SILVER CHANTER

It would seem that not every one of the sons of that famous family, the MacCrimmons of Dunvegan, was gifted with unusual skill in playing the pipes, for one there was, a small slight youth, whose attempts to play disappointed his father. He was the third son, and although his elder brothers could play almost as well as their father, his attempts were no better than those of the tinkers behind the roadside hedge.

He had fine hands, sensitive fingers and a love of good music. But it seemed that it was to be his lot to listen, while his brothers played their wonderful music. Often he would go off to the lonely moors and practise upon an old black chanter, yet it seemed that the improvement would never come. His fingers were not nimble enough, and the music that came was halting and uncertain.

One day he was on the point of throwing the chanter

into the depths of a little brown lochan, dappled with blossoming water-lilies, when a maiden suddenly appeared from the shadow of a high rock. There was something in the light that played in her golden hair, in the tilt of her little head, in the grace of her approach, that made the youth a little afraid. Moreover she wore a strange gown of the brightest green, the green of the first rowan leaves, from which came the dye the fairies used (so it was said) to dye their clothes.

'I heard the notes you played on the little black chanter,' she said. 'Let me hear them again, young man.'

Young MacCrimmon apologised for his lack of skill, but the maiden insisted that he should play. When it was over, the maiden smiled.

'What is your greatest wish?' she asked.

'To be the equal of my father as a piper,' replied the youth without hesitation.

'Even if it brings a measure of unhappiness?' asked the maiden.

'Even if it means that, and the life that is in me,' insisted the young man.

'Then take this,' she continued, taking from the folds of her green gown, a little silver chanter.

The youth accepted the gift with trembling hands. He had never seen anything so beautiful before as the instrument she offered.

'Now set it to your lips, but let my fingers teach you the notes you must play,' smiled the strange damsel. The youth did as he was bid, while she rested her arms on his shoulders and touched the chanter with her fingers. The music that came was the most beautiful that young MacCrimmon had ever heard. 'Now,' went on the maiden when the lesson was over, 'the silver chanter is yours for a year and a day. It will give to your fingers the touch that will make you the greatest piper in Scotland. But you must return with it after a year and a day have passed, to the cave by the little brown tarn yonder where I shall await your coming.'

MacCrimmon promised, and went home with the fairy's gift held tightly in his fingers. But before he reached his father's house the urge came to him to try his skill and play the music the maiden had taught him. To his joy the melody he played was even more wonderful than the one he had learned on the moor. It brought his father and his two brothers to the door, and to be sure, they were astonished at the gift that had come so suddenly to the young man. ' Three sons I have,' cried his father, ' but this one before me is the greatest piper of them all ! ' As indeed he was, for his fingers ran on, bringing out sweetness and sorrow and an almost unearthly joy at times from the silver chanter. And when it came to playing the big pipe, there was no doubt of it, there was no man his equal in all the world.

But the day came when young MacCrimmon was duty bound to return the fairy's gift. He set out across the moor with his father and his brothers, until they reached the lochan of the lilies where the fairy dwelt in the cave, But when he reached the shadows of the great rock he halted the others. ' I will go alone now,' he said.

' And when you return, my son, let us hope the magic will still be there in your fingers, even if the silver chanter is no longer with you.'

The young man then went into the depths of the cave, his fingers playing the strangest, saddest music that had ever been heard in the island of Skye, music that had all the sorrows of the world in it, yet was bewitching to the ear. The listeners in the sunshine stood as the piper went deeper and deeper into the earth, his piping becoming fainter and fainter. ' MacCrimmon will return no more,' the echoes seemed to say.

And that, in truth, is how the legend must end. For although the last echo never died, but lingers in the farthest passages of MacCrimmon's Cave for those who have the hearing ear, the young MacCrimmon never returned to the earth and the sunshine.

And if you doubt my tale, that MacCrimmon still plays his silver chanter somewhere in that enchanted cave, then stand in the shadow of the rock by the lily lochan, which is not so very far from the great Castle of Dunvegan, and listen. Some say who have heard it that the sound is the sorrowing of the sea ; others hear in the whisper of music the wind in the young rowan-trees ; or the breath of spring across the waters of the lochan of the lilies. But whatever it is, the music is sweet to hear.

BALACH BEAG NA DEISE GUIRME
(*Little boy blue*)

> ' Ille bhig na deise guirme,
> Thig is seid an dudach ;
> An crodh air feadh an arbhair ;
> Sa' chluan tha na caoraich.
> Ach cait a bheil an gille beag
> Bu choir bhith toirt an aire orr' ?
> ' Na shineadh ris an dig fheoir
> Is srann aige 'na chadal !

*

Teagasg ga thoirt do mhnaoi bhuirb, mar bhuille ùird air iarunn fuar.
Chastising a termagant is like hammering cold iron.

22

8 DOMHNULL AND THE BAY STALLION

DOMHNULL OG was an orphan. When his mother died his father married again. But the second marriage lasted only a few years, and when Domhnull was twelve years old, his father fell ill and died.

The little boy lived with his stepmother in a hovel on the island of Tiree. His life was a hard one. Summer and winter he went barefoot. No work was considered too hard for him, and often he went hungry to bed. As he grew up he came to know the lash of his stepmother's tongue, and the hardness of her heart. He decided to run away as soon as he was old enough.

One evening as he brought the cows home from the pasture he passed close to the shores of Loch an Eilin. A bay stallion was grazing by the waters. The animal was a fine one, unharnessed except for a black bridle, and quite unconscious of the approach of the boy. Domhnull hid behind the foremost cow, and so was able to come very close to the stallion. Then, when the herd came abreast the animal, the lad skipped out and seized it by the bridle.

Now had he stopped to think Domhnull might have been more careful of approaching the horse, for as often as not, such creatures usually proved to be water kelpies. But the boy held fast to the bridle while the creature reared and plunged in its struggles to escape.

When it seemed that the boy must surely be trampled under the flying hooves, or dragged to his death in the waters of the little loch, the bridle loosened. It slipped suddenly from the creature's head, and Domhnull was left holding the bridle while the beast plunged into the loch and vanished.

The lad was disappointed. He would have loved

23

to have captured so fiery and handsome a steed. But at the same time he gave thanks to Providence for being still alive. Besides he had gained possession of a fine, black bridle, such as few boys were lucky enough to have. But, he thought, it would be wise to say nothing of his adventure to his stepmother. As for the bridle it would be better hidden.

He found a cranny in the rocks, and was on the point of concealing his treasure when a voice spoke in his ear : ' Bridle the false one you call *mathair*,[1] Domhnull, before the black-cock seeks its roost. From that minute you will be master.' The boy turned in fear and amazement, for it was the bridle that had spoken. Either that or his imagination was playing him tricks. Bridle his stepmother indeed ! He would be the bold and foolish one to try that on the wry-faced termagant ! But he determined to take the bridle home with him and hide it in the peat stack.

On reaching the cottage he found the woman dozing over the fire. Softly he made his approach. Surely this was the opportunity to obey the whisper he had heard ! He brought the bridle from the folds of his tattered shirt, and dropped it over her head.

She awoke at once, screaming loudly as she struggled to her feet and stumbled outside. But the bridle held firmly in its place. And by the time the boy followed her to the path she had been transformed from human shape to that of a sheltie [2] that trembled and pawed the earth. He set his hand on the creature's mane and the sheltie made no attempt to bolt.

The bridle had spoken truly. He had the woman under his spell. Thrice he mounted and rode the animal round the house, and he laughed for joy. He was indeed master, and master he would remain, he knew, as long as the bridle held.

[1] *mathair*, mother   [2] *sheltie*, small horse

But the horse had still to be shod. So Dumhnull set off to the blacksmith, where after many words of admiration had been spoken in favour of the lad's fine horse, he saw to it that the creature was well shod.

From that day the sheltie was put to work on the croft, and each night it came home weary and glad to rest. But it was clear that its spirit was broken. Each day it grew leaner. And in spite of a healthy appetite its hide hung loosely on its bony frame. At length the lad could no longer bear the pain and sorrow in the poor creature's eyes. One morning he took the bridle from its head and threw it far into Loch an Eilin.

In a twinkling the spell was broken. The sheltie vanished, and in its place crouched the cruel stepmother, overcome with weeping. Domhnull bade her rise, but she held out her hands and feet. The iron horseshoes were still nailed in place.

The blacksmith was astonished to see Domhnull Og returning to the smiddy with his stepmother shod with iron. He was even more astounded to recognise the shoes he had fitted to Domhnull's sheltie. The boy explained what had happened and the woman begged that the nails be drawn as quickly as possible. At last the blacksmith understood, and set about his gruesome task.

No sound did she make until the last nail was drawn, then the woman uttered a scream of agony, falling in a faint which lasted the night long.

From that day Domhnull's life was changed. In regaining her human form, his stepmother had lost all bitterness and hatred for her stepson. And the legend ends with the words that they continued to live in that happy and contented state until Domhnull reached manhood and went off to seek his fortune elsewhere.

THERE were few living between Ben Cruachan and the sea who did not know Calum Ciotach.   He was only a wee bit of a man, with a beard like a billy-goat's, but no hair at all on the top of his head.   He was called Calum Ciotach [1] because he was left-handed, but his neighbours called him other things as well, because for all his talk about his strength and cleverness and the great thing it was to be left-handed, Calum Ciotach was a lazy man.   If he could not find an easy way to do a thing, then he just wouldn't do that thing at all !

One day the heel came off his shoe.   Nobody would mend it for him, so he had to do the job himself.   As you can imagine, he was not in the best of tempers, for he had hit his fingers more often than the nails.   Moreover it was a fine day and he would much rather have been outside, lying on the grass doing nothing.

Just as he was about to throw the shoe and the hammer across the kitchen, there came a tapping at the door.   Before Calum could rise and lift the latch someone outside began very softly to play a fiddle.   He peeped through the window to see a little man, smaller than himself, playing on a brown fiddle.   When he opened the door the little man held out his hat.

' Bless the house, Calum Ciotach ! Will you spare a copper for the fiddler ? ' he asked.

' Away with you, tinker ! ' replied Calum.   ' It is the poor man I am, with little enough for myself.'

' Is that not the great pity ! When I saw your fine house, Calum Ciotach, I said to my fiddle, " The man that lives here will be knowing a fine tune when he hears one.   You will do your best to please the gentleman."   And sure enough the fiddle never tried harder.'

---

[1] *ciotach*, left-handed

' What nonsense is this, tinker ! To hear you talk one would be thinking it was the fiddle and not yourself that made the music ! '

' Hush ! ' whispered the fiddler. ' By the Seven Sleepers, don't be miscalling the fiddle, or the fairies who brought it to my doorstep will be putting the spell on us ! '

' Away with you ! Many a fiddle have I seen, but never a plainer one than this. A fairy fiddle indeed ! '

' Very well, Calum Ciotach. Put it under your chin and try it for yourself.'

Now Calum had never tried to play a fiddle before. But when he began to scrape the bow back and forward across the strings, his eyebrows shot up and his mouth opened wide. For, sure enough, the fiddle began to play the sweetest, merriest music he had ever heard. The fingers of his left hand were dancing on

27

the strings as nimbly as the little *drilleachan* [1] on the summer shore, and there he was, playing the strathspey of Donald Gorm, Macuisne the Chief's own piper!

' Oho! ' he cried, ' hear me! To think I have been able to play the fiddle all the years, and myself not knowing it at all! A fairy fiddle, fiddle-sticks! A stupid man might believe your story, tinker, but Calum Ciotach is not a fool. Fine I know it is not the fiddle but the cleverness that is in my left hand that makes the music. Listen to this! '

Calum began to play again, and this time the music was so sweet and sad that before he had finished the tears were rolling down his own whiskers.

' Aye, it is the beautiful fiddle, and it suits me well, tinker. I will be pleased to give you a silver sixpence for it,' said Calum, taking the coin from his pocket.

The fiddler looked at the sixpence, then he looked at Calum with a queer twist of a smile. ' I will take your sixpence, sir. But there is something I must tell you about the fiddle. See to it that you are never boastful or conceited about that fine left hand of yours, for it is the jealous fiddle, and trouble will come to you if you forget.'

But Calum Ciotach had already shut the door in the stranger's face.

That very day Calum Ciotach put on his best bonnet, and with his fiddle under his arm he went off down the road. By and by he reached the village.

' Where are you off to, Calum Ciotach? ' he was asked.

' I am going to play my fiddle before Macuisne the Chief,' said Calum. ' And when he hears my music, then it is myself who will be taking his silver and playing for him, instead of Donald Gorm.'

[1] *drilleachan*, sandpiper

' Indeed ! We never knew you were a fiddler. Let us hear your music, man.'

When Calum began to play the villagers crowded round in admiration and wonder. ' Never have we heard a fiddle better played ! ' they cried as soon as he had finished.

' Och, it is nothing if you have the touch,' declared the conceited little man. ' I have all the skill in my fine left hand. See how easy it is for me,' he went on, lifting the fiddle once again. But before he could begin, a string snapped and struck his face.

' Oh, oh, oh ! ' he cried, dancing with the pain. ' My nose is cut in two halves ! '

' Ho, ho, ho ! That was a good one, Calum ! Your fine left hand it must have been ! ' laughed the villagers.

Calum hurried off angry and dismayed. He tried to tie the broken string, but the knot would not hold. Yet when he drew the bow across the remaining strings he found little difference in the music, and he hurried to Macuisne's castle.

He strode boldly to the door and knocked three times.

' Who is there ? ' demanded a voice.

' It is Calum Ciotach, Macuisne's fiddler.'

' Macuisne's fiddler ? There is no such man,' said the keeper of the door, coming out to see.

' Ah, but there soon will be, for I am the greatest fiddler in all Scotland. When the Chief hears my music it will be myself and no longer Donald Gorm who will play at his table and his feasting. And the fame of my nimble left hand will be known from the sea to the sea.'

No sooner had Calum made his boast than the second string snapped. This time it struck the keeper of the door.

'Woe! It is blinded I am!' he roared. 'The stranger has blinded me!'

His shouts brought the Chief's men running with drawn swords. Last to come was Donald Gorm. When he heard of Calum Ciotach's boasting he spoke: 'Let us hear if your music is suited for the presence of the Chief, stranger.'

This time Calum's music was not quite as merry, and he made haste to apologise. 'Give me a minute longer and I will show you what my fine left hand can do, Donald Gorm.' And with that the third string snapped!

Donald Gorm clapped a hand to his chin and screamed, 'To the dungeons with him!' The foolish little man was bundled down a narrow stair and dropped into a dark cell along with his fiddle. 'There now, my fine fiddler, let us hear what your fine left hand can do now!'

For three whole days Calum Ciotach lay in the dungeon. At last he saw how foolish he had been. What was it the fiddler had said? 'See to it that you are neither boastful nor conceited about that fine left hand of yours, for it is a jealous fiddle.' Alas, and because of his vanity, trouble had surely come to him in plenty.

He laid his hand upon the broken fiddle. To his surprise the strings were whole again! Calum lifted it and began to play in the darkness. And the music he played was sweeter than ever before.

By and by it reached the ears of the Chief. 'Who is that playing on a fiddle, Donald Gorm?' he demanded, cocking an ear.

'It is one Calum Ciotach, a wretch we have in the dungeon, Macuisne.'

'I like his music fine. Bring him here and let him play for me.'

30

From that day nobody who heard Calum Ciotach's music could resist it. It set Macuisne's foot tapping, and even Donald Gorm fell silent in admiration. Calum was pardoned, and he shared with Donald Gorm the honour of providing the Chief with music on all occasions.

Today Macuisne's castle stands in ruins. Some folk who have gone there on a windy night say they have heard the sweet music of the fairy fiddle.

But maybe it is only the wind in the empty chimney-place.

*

Nam faighteadh ceud sagairt gun bhith sanntach ;
Ceud taillear gun bhith sunndach ;
Ceud greusaich gun bhith breugach ;
Ceud figheadair gun bhith bradach ;
Ceud gobha gun bhith paiteach ;
Is ceud cailleach nach robh riamh air cheilidh ;
Chuireadh iad an crun air an righ gun aon bhuille.

(If there could be found—
A hundred priests who were not greedy ;
A hundred tailors who were not rollicking ;
A hundred shoemakers who were not untruthful ;
A hundred weavers who were not thievish ;
A hundred blacksmiths who were not thirsty ;
A hundred old women who were never gossiping ;
They could put the crown on the king's head without striking a blow.)

PHARIC ANGUS was young and strong. With his own two hands he had built a small house that was warm and snugly thatched against the worst of the winter's storms. And his croft was flourishing, so that in the spring of the year he had little trouble in persuading Mari, the daughter of a distant crofter, to be his wife.

One day in the autumn, as the shadows were lengthening across the uncut corn in his field, Pharic Angus was crossing a dry-dyke that kept out the neighbours' sheep. Fraoch, an old and faithful dog, followed close at his heels. As the young crofter prepared to leap to the ground he was astonished to see a large brown hare stretched out in sleep in the long grass.

He signed silently to the dog, which immediately sprang to the ground not a yard from the sleeping hare. But the hare awoke before the dog reached it, and bounded off in panic. But not before Fraoch's teeth had nipped it in the small of the back. The frightened creature screamed piteously as it fled uphill, Fraoch labouring to catch up, until he was so breathless that he was forced to stop.

The hare reached a rushy mound, where it stopped suddenly, as hares will do, sat erect and motionless, and looked back at its pursuer that limped back to the young crofter. And there was something in the creature's lingering gaze that struck a curious chill in the heart of Pharic Angus. It was as if a cloud had crossed the face of the sun, leaving the world suddenly cold, or, as if an icy breath blew from the mountain-tops. Pharic Angus shuddered, called Fraoch to heel sharply, and went home.

[1] *maigheach*, a hare

32

The incident appeared to be the start of a series of troubles, opening in a small way with the sudden dourness of the fire in the hearth. With only a little glow would it burn, nor would the bellows raise more than a spark and a short-lived flame. Then the well dried up ; the cheese rotted as soon as it was made ; milk went sour in the basins ; the cow went lame, and every third lamb pined on the hill and died. At length Mari herself fell ill with a fever and Pharic Angus became desperate.

'What has happened to this place ! ' he cried. ' Ill luck comes with each dawn. It would seem that my home, my cattle-beasts and all that I possess are under some evil spell. I will see what advice Magnus has to give.'

Magnus, the old wise one, heard Pharic Angus's story of ill fortune and disaster. ' Misfortune followed the drying of the drinking-well, Pharic Angus,' said Magnus.

' It did not,' replied Pharic Angus. ' It came before that when the fire would not smoor and was slow to cook the pot. Now even the peat that is dry to its core burns black and without heat.'

' Then,' said Magnus, nodding his wrinkled head, ' return you to your own place. Let the peat that smoulders in the hearth be taken seven times *deiseal* [1] about the walls. For your fortune is going out with the fire, across the threshold, in unsained [2] hands.'

Pharic Angus returned home to his ailing wife, a disappointed man. Magnus was wise as everyone recognised. But there were times when his words would not make sense. Who was there to take the fire from the hearth in these parts ? The *bodach's* wits were surely growing feeble.

---

[1] *deiseal*, in the direction of the sun
[2] *unsained*, without a blessing to ward off evil

Mari listened in silence to Pharic's account of his visit. Next day with a great effort she rose from her fever and returned to her housework. She would not turn aside from whatever would come to them, be it good or evil. But the spell remained unbroken. That very day a boulder from the hillside crushed Pharic's foot. For several days he was forced to sit by the fire, complaining bitterly that the rain must surely come before the corn was cut.

' It is for me to help, Pharic Angus,' said Mari. ' Let me cut with the sickle, and if the strength has returned to your foot, then you may tie the sheaves.' At first her husband was reluctant to agree. But Mari insisted that the fine weather must come to an end very soon, and that they should set off next morning.

So early in the morning they left the house. Pharic Angus limped slowly, slower even than the old dog Fraoch, and when he had gone but a short distance he was already tired and glad to rest. While resting he happened to turn his head back towards the door, and he saw a movement there as of someone entering the house. ' Mari ! ' he called softly to his wife a little way ahead. ' Haste ye back to the house, and see if the door is open or shut.'

' Surely it will be as I left it, Pharic Angus—with the bolt closing it ! ' she replied in surprise. ' Why do you ask so strange a question ? '

In reply Pharic Angus told her quickly what he had seen. Mari then hastened to the door. To her surprise it was open. She crossed the threshold to meet a wizened hag in the act of leaving the kitchen, with a lighted peat held in a pair of black tongs. Mari reached out to take the tongs from the stranger, but she was flung hard against the wall.

Pharic Angus, limping at his wife's heels, reached the doorway in time to see a lean brown hare bound

out of the house. It passed him swiftly, loping towards
the moor. But Fraoch was there waiting. He seized
the animal as it passed and in an instant it lay dead
on the pathway.

Husband and wife recalled the words of Magnus,
the wise one. The witch, who had taken the form of a
mountain hare to work her evil, had taken the fire
from their hearth in 'unsained' hands. With her
death the flame of the peat fire was no longer in
danger. And from that day, as events proved, the
spell was broken. Pharic Angus prospered, and his
hearth was warm, winter and summer.

35

AN AM AN ÉIGIN DEARBHAR NE CAIDREAN
A friend in need is a friend indeed

Robin Redbreast was caught fast in the thorn thicket. ' Set me free ! Set me free ! ' he pleaded. Two birds heard his cries—the jay and the crossbill. The jay flew into the wood, afraid that he might be caught himself. But the crossbill set to work to break the cruel thorns, rending and tearing until he had set the captive free.

For his cowardice the jay is despised by birds and man. But the crossbill whose beak became crooked and broken lives happily in the forests of the north. With his crooked bill he is well able to strip the seeds from the cones on which he feeds.

*

Am fear a phosas bean posaidh e dragh.
He who marries a wife marries trouble.

ii THE WHITE MOTH

DONALD the fisherman sat at his lonely fireside and supped the last of his meal. When it was finished he set aside the bowl and stirred the embers of the fire. It was midsummer and far from cold. Evening sunshine was still streaming through the leaves of the green briar bush outside the window, and laying a broad track of golden light across the loch. But Donald was a lonely man, and found companionship in the dancing flames.

For a long time he sat quite still, half-way between sleeping and waking. Presently he was roused by a soft tapping on the window. He looked up to see a white moth dancing on the panes. Sometimes it rested momentarily on the petals of the roses or on the narrow sill, but always it returned to flutter on the glass as if intent on entering the house.

Donald rose at last and opened the window. At once the moth flew over his head and circled the little room while the fisherman stooped to light the cruisie.[1] No sooner had the flame appeared than the moth swept from the rafters. It hovered over the flame then fell scorched on the floor. A sudden flash of light blinded the young man, and when he looked again the shrivelled moth had disappeared and in its place stood a maiden dressed in a white garment.

' Who are you ? ' he asked in amazement.

The maiden smiled. ' I am the moth,' she replied. ' If you will make me your bride, I will love you forever, and you will no longer be lonely, day or night.'

Donald looked upon the maiden and was bewitched by her great beauty. They became man and wife, and in the days that followed Donald was a happy and contented man.

' Be sure that you tell no-one how I came to you in the form of a white moth. Let the fire be the only light within the house, Donald. For the flame of the cruisie that made me woman must never again be lighted. It will draw me to it and I will be destroyed.' Donald heeded her wish. He told no-one of her strange coming. Each evening they sat in the light of the fire, and the cruisie remained unlit by the window.

Now there lived close by a widow woman who had one daughter. This girl had longed to be the wife of the fisherman. When she learned that he had been wed, she came often in the darkness to look with bitterness upon them as they sat together by the fire.

---

[1] *cruisie*, simple oil lamp

She grew to hate the maiden who had come to steal her lover, grudging her beauty, and longing to take her place.

One night as she listened, she saw Donald rise to light the cruisie. She saw how his wife stayed him, and heard her tell him again how the flame would bring about her death. The widow's daughter ran home, unable to understand the warning she had overheard. But she knew that it was surely in her power to take vengeance if she could enter the house.

Next evening she returned to the fisherman's house. The dusk was gathering, and Donald had not yet returned from the sea. She tapped softly on the door and when his wife opened it she begged to be allowed to enter, confessing that a sickness had come upon her.

The young wife led her to a seat in the kitchen and went to bring a cup of water. When she had gone the widow's daughter made haste to light the cruisie with a coal from the fire. She set it on the table so that its light fell on the threshold. When the fisherman's wife returned, the cup fell from her hands and she tried to shield her eyes and turn away. But she could not resist the light. It drew her slowly on until at last she stretched her hands and touched the heart of the flame.

Immediately the light guttered and went out. The widow's daughter screamed, for the maiden fell upon the table. Her body became a small shrivelled thing that slowly transformed itself into a white moth.

At that moment Donald the fisherman opened the door. The moth was lifted in the sudden draught; and before the door closed again, it had flown swiftly into the night. When he saw that his wife was gone, he demanded to know what had become of her. When the widow's daughter told him what had happened he thrust her aside, and ran into the darkness, crying for his wife to return.

Donald the fisherman himself was never seen again. But in the morning a small white moth with broken shrivelled wings was found dead at the roots of the green briar bush.

12 FEILEAGAN BEAG

Feileagan beag, Feileagan !
Bha Mor Ni' Ruaraidh 's Feileagan
Is Iain Mor Bochusragan
Cur surd ro Nighean Bochosragan
Feileagan beag, bideach gun lochd
Fad na raith gheamhraith anns an t-sop
Trath thig an raith' shamraidh seinnidh e port
'S o bharr nan neoinean olaidh e deoch.

Latha dhomh 's mi deanamh cruaich'
Feasgar foghair 's cach a' buain
De chuala mi le mo chluais
Ach gaoir am bruaich aig Feileagan
Feileagan beag, Feileagan. . . .

Tha taigh mor aig Feileagan
Air cul a chnoic dochomhradain
Taraidh ceud nan ceudan ann
'S cha tarainn fein 'nam aonar ann
Feileagan beag, Feileagan. . . .

LITTLE KILTIE

[The 'little tartaned fellow' referred to in the poem on p. 39 is none other than the bee with his colourful stripes. This poem from Gairloch, Ross-shire, is really a rhyming riddle.]

Little tartaned fellow—
Making up to the daughter of Roderick Bee
And big John of Bochosragan,
Stirring the daughter of Bochosragan.
Wee, wee fellow without guile
Throughout the winter hid in straw ;
When comes the summer he sings a song
And from the daisy-heads takes a sip.
Once as I was building a stack
On an autumn afternoon as the others were reaping,
What should reach my ear
But the humming of a bee from a bank.
The bee has a spacious house
At the back of the rugged hill ;
Hundreds upon hundreds will enter it
Yet I could not alone go in.

13 THE GLEN OF WEEPING

GLENCOE, sometimes called the Glen of Weeping, is seldom spoken of in the Highlands without recalling memories of the massacre of the MacDonalds.

William of Orange decided to subdue the warring clans north of the Highland line. He ordered that each chieftain appear at Inveraray before the first day of the year 1692, and swear allegiance to the Crown. MacIain, chief of the MacDonalds, misunderstood the order. He made his way to Fort William and on the appointed day presented himself to the Governor, only to discover his mistake. By the time MacIain reached Inveraray four days had passed, four fateful days in which his enemies had seized their chance to take action against the clan.

One month later, on 1 February, one hundred and twenty-eight 'redcoats' drawn from the hated Campbells of Argyll marched into Glencoe. They pretended that there was no room for them in the stronghold of Fort William, and begged food and shelter from MacIain. The old chief made them welcome and entertained them for a fortnight with true Highland hospitality, little knowing the true purpose of their visit.

Rising early in the morning of 13 February Campbell and his men repaid the Macdonalds kindness by treacherously killing thirty-eight of the clan, and causing almost twice that number to flee into the mountains where they perished in a snowstorm. Yet the fierce blizzard was more compassionate than the king's men, for by detaining a second detachment of troops from Fort William it enabled the scattered remnants of the clan to make their way through the passes to safety.

Many legends have grown round the infamous deed. One story tells of a soldier who learned on the previous day what was in store for the MacDonalds. This man invited his host Maceanruig mor nan Feadan ('big Henderson of the Chanters') to walk with him down the Glen at sunset. When they reached a boulder by the track the soldier stopped. 'Grey stone of the Glen,' he said, 'you have every right to be where you are, but if you could be knowing what will happen here tonight, it is not here you would be staying.' Maceanruig was puzzled, but the soldier would say no more lest he break his oath of secrecy.

When the incident was related to MacIain, the old man would not believe treachery was intended. But Maceanruig and the two sons of the chieftain were suspicious, and they decided to remain awake and alert. The blizzard was at its height when they heard a musket fired. It was the signal for the slaughter to be started, and they slipped into hiding. Meanwhile the first cottages were burning and the redcoats on their rounds striking down the unsuspecting families as they slept. One party of soldiers seeking survivors, saw a woman running with her child across the moor. The officer in command ordered one of his men to hunt her down and kill her with her child. The soldier soon caught the distracted woman, but instead of putting her to death he led her into hiding, sacrificing instead the dog that trotted at her heels. When he returned with his bayonet smeared with the animal's blood his leader was satisfied that his commands had been carried out satisfactorily.

Many years afterwards an old man came into the Glen. He was given food and shelter by a crofter, and as he took his supper by the peat fire, he heard again the grim story of the killing. When the story was finished he admitted that as a Highlander from Inverness he had taken part in the business. The crofter said no more, but he resolved to take vengeance before the dawn. The old man, however, went on to tell how he had refrained from killing anyone himself. Instead he had secretly helped a woman with her child of escape. But he was unable to tell if they had succeeded in escaping afterwards with their lives.

The MacDonald rose from his seat in amazement. 'Aye indeed they did escape!' he cried, shaking the visitor by the hand. 'That woman was my own mother, and I am the child she bore in her arms. Until the day she died she was praying for your well-being in this world, and for your soul in the hereafter. You are welcome, man of Inverness, to hospitality in this house as long as you please to remain.'

To this day two stones may be seen in Glencoe, one of which is known as the Signal Rock where the musket was fired. The other, Henderson's Stone, is said to be the very stone where the warning was given to Maceanruig on the eve of the massacre.

AN RUIDEAL

Tri casan nach gluais
Da chluais nach cluinn
Beul mor nach bruidhinn.

A RIDDLE

Three legs that cannot move
Two ears that cannot hear
A big mouth that cannot speak.

[a three-legged pot]

14 THE FOX AND THE WOLF

THE fox was lean with hunger, but the wolf he met in the wood was leaner and almost famished. The wolf decided to accompany the fox so that he might seize, or at least share whatever the clever fox might find to eat.

This arrangement did not suit the fox one little bit. Presently he spied a bull grazing on the hill. ' Now, here's an odd thing ! ' he said to his companion. ' A bull with its name written on its haunches. *Chan 'eil*

43

mi am sgoilear 's chan ail leam a bhith.[1]   But you
can read, my friend.   Would you care to read the name
for me ? '

   The wolf, flattered by his sly companion, approached
the bull.   He went right up, pretending to scrutinise
the bull's haunches.   The bull struck out of course and
put an end to the wolf.   And the fox went his way
satisfied.   When he caught a rabbit he had his supper
all to himself.

*

Gheibh as t-uaibhreach leigeadh an uair airde e.
The proud will be humbled at their highest (or, Pride
comes before a fall).

15   THE BROWNIE AND THE LITTLE BLACK PIG

In the heart of Argyll there lived a chief who had one
son.   The youth grew up to be proud and selfish,
giving little thought to the comfort and well-being
of others.

   In the forest near by lived a *bodach* or brownie, so
old that his beard was grey as the lichen, and his back
more crooked than the thorn-tree.   One day as he
trudged home with a great bundle of sticks on his back,
Braun, son of the chief, galloped from the forest on
a proud steed.   Before the *bodach* could turn aside he
was thrown into the briars.

   When Braun saw him sprawling in the bushes, his
short legs kicking feebly, he threw up his head and
laughed.   But he made no effort to help the old fellow.
Presently he tired of watching and set spurs to his
horse.   The startled creature dashed a cloud of dust

[1] I am not a scholar, and don't wish to be

44

into the brownie's eyes, so that once again he fell into the thorns, his sticks scattered everywhere.

When at length the brownie dragged himself out of the ditch, and gathered his sticks for the third time that day, he set the last one in a rut. He covered it with grass and spoke to it in a strange language. Then he went his way.

Next morning Braun rode through the forest as usual. But his steed touched the hidden stick with a forefoot, so that it stumbled. The young man was pitched into the briars, while the horse cantered off on its way home. Then when the bushes parted, lo ! it was not Braun that appeared, but a small black pig blinking small eyes in the sunlight.

' *Muc bheg !* ' [1] said a voice, and the little pig turned to see the brownie. ' Little-black-one-with-the-flat-snout that was once the son of the chief, yesterday it was I who was cast into the thorns in the ditch. Today it is you who crawl out in the form of a beast. Go into the world and know the suffering of the humble. And let your lesson be truly learned.'

' But,' wailed Braun in a grunting voice, ' must I spend the rest of my life trotting on four feet, my nose to the earth, and my ears flapping ? '

' That you must surely do until you have had your lesson and answered a riddle.'

' Then tell me the riddle, *bodach*.'

> ' The crooked stick upon your head,
> The pebble from the river's bed,
> The leaf that crowns the elder-tree,
> The maiden's kiss to set you free.'

And with that the brownie vanished into the shades of the wood.

[1] *muc bheg*, little pig

45

The little black pig went slowly down the road, pondering the brownie's strange riddle. His feet were raising puffs of dust that made his eyes smart. By and by a cow appeared and made him step aside. A dog that smelled him coming barked and chased him into the forest. If only he could master the first line of the riddle he would be a little comforted!

A man spied him, and before he could escape, the man had him caught in a noose. He was dragged towards a cottage, but he fought and struggled so hard that his captor became angry.

'Very well, little warrior, perhaps a beating will keep you trotting!' he cried, lifting a branch from the ground, and striking the pigling on the head. Immediately the branch leapt into the air and the man let go the rope. He had fulfilled the first words of the brownie's riddle, for the branch was as crooked as a dog's hind leg, and the little pig escaped into the forest.

He never stopped running until he had reached the broad river. If only he could lift a *doirneag* [1] from its bed; he would be yet another step towards becoming Braun again! He snuffled and poked his head under water. He tried to walk under the current,

[1] *doirneag*, a little stone

46

but each time he floated back to the surface, and the pebbles at the bottom were as far away as ever.

For many days he lingered by the river, envying the fish and the otters their skill in swimming. He never reached the river bed, but it was very pleasant to wallow in the cool water while the sun blazed overhead.

One morning he woke to find the river-bed almost dry—there was only a trickle of water spilling over the rocks. In no time he had waddled in to grasp a shining pebble which he carried off joyfully in his mouth. He had accomplished the second task and his heart was lighter.

His next task was to find the elder-tree. And find it he did at the end of the day. But it seemed so high that its branches were poking up into the clouds. He tried to climb the branches but his short legs and fat body were not the right shape for climbing trees, and he rolled over each time into the grass.

It was then that the first drops of rain began to fall, first lightly, then in a mighty flood as thunder and lightning rolled and flashed in the darkening sky. The elder-tree sheltered him as inch by inch the river rose in spate until it reached the roots of the elder-tree. At length the roots were so loose that the tree tilted and fell headlong. The little pig gave a cry of joy and snatched the leaf that crowned it! He had only one more task to do.

But the more he thought of the maiden's kiss that he had to earn, the more unhappy he became. He looked at the ugly reflection of his own head in the water, and knew he would

47

have to travel far to persuade a maiden to soil her lips. The little pig was humble for the first time in his life, and he began to weep.

Suddenly he heard someone weeping as bitterly as he wept himself. It was an old woman who had fallen into a thicket, and he saw that she was blind. At first she was afraid of the grunting piglet, but when he caught the hem of her skirt and began to lead her towards the road she followed him gladly. The two strange companions wandered on until they came in sight of a cottage.

Presently a dog barked. ' That is the voice of Gruff ! ' cried the old woman happily. The door of the cottage opened and the woman's grand-daughter came running to greet them.

' Glad am I to know you are safe, Grandma ! I have searched the hills and the hollows in vain, and now you come home with a little black pig ! '

' I am home, Mary. But for this little black pig that I cannot see I would have perished in the forest.'

The maiden embraced her grandmother, then impulsively caught up the piglet and kissed it on its ugly snout. It fell at once at her feet, but this time when it rose it was no longer in the form of a pig but as Braun, the son of the chief. The spell the brownie had laid upon him was broken.

Before the moon changed, Braun and Mary, grand-daughter of the blind woman, were wed. The brownie, hearing the news, was well content, and he gave them both his blessing. And it is told that when Braun succeeded his father, there was none who ruled more wisely or with more consideration for his fellows.

[In the following little poems the Gaelic words and phrases have been excellently chosen to represent the songs and call-notes of the birds.]

ADHARCAN

Till, till ; till, till !
Na creach mo nead !
Na creach mo nead !
Iomachd gun teachd dhut !
Iomachd gun teachd dhut !
A bhraidein !   A bhraidein !

THE LAPWING

Turn, turn ; turn, turn !
Do not harry my nest !
Do not harry my nest !
Begone and return not !
Begone and return not !
You thief !   You thief !

49

AN FHEADAG

Is mor mo dhiobhail ;
Is mor mo dhiobhail ;
Tha mi cianail ;
Tha mi cianail ;
Fag leam fhin mi ;
Fag leam fhin mi.

THE GOLDEN PLOVER

Great is my loss ;
Great is my loss ;
I am sad ;
I am sad ;
Leave me alone ;
Leave me alone.

GILLE-BRIDE

Eoin bhig !   Eoin bhig !
Bi glic !   Bi glic !
Fo dhion !   Fo dhion !

THE OYSTER-CATCHER

Little bird !   Little bird !
Be wise !   Be wise !
Hide !   Hide !

AN COLMAN

Chan ann de'm chuideachd thu ;
Chan ann de'm chuideachd thu ;
Tha mo chul riut ;
Tha mo chul riut ;
Nam b'ann de'm chuideachd thu
Chan itheadh tu siud
Gun mo chuid a thoirt dhomhsa,
Gun mo chuid a thoirt dhomhsa.

THE DOVE

I am not of your kind ;
I am not of your kind ;
I turn my back on you ;
I turn my back on you ;
Were you one of us
You would not eat yon
Without giving me my portion,
Without giving me my portion.

AN COILEACH MOR IS AN COILEACH BEAG

An Coileach Mor : An aithne dhutsa co mi, a
  Dhomhaill ?
An Coileach Beag : Mac circe ! Mac circe !

THE BIG COCKEREL AND THE LITTLE COCKEREL

Big fellow [*proudly*] : Know you who I am, Donald ?
Little fellow [*unimpressed*] : A hen's son ! A hen's
  son !

AM BRU-DHEARG

Big, big, bigein !
Co creach mo neadan ?
Ma's e gille beag e
Cuiridh mi le creig e !
Ma's e gille mor e
Cuiridh mi le lon e !
Ach, ma's fear beag gun cheill e,
Gun gleidheadh Dia d'a mhathair fein e !

THE REDBREAST

Chirp, chirp, chirrup !
Who robbed my nest ?
If it was a little boy
Throw him over the rock !
If it was a big boy
Throw him in the bog !
But if he be a little one without sense
May God preserve him for his mother !

Ailean nan Creach,[1] chief of Clan Cameron, was a great warrior, and in his day he had brought about the death of many men. One day he had a premonition of his own end, and the prospect gave him cause to repent of his earlier misdeeds.

He went secretly to the house of a witch and begged her help to save his soul from purgatory. The witch heard his confession, then told him what he must do on the morrow.

Ailean took her advice. With one of his clansmen, a sack of peats and sticks, and a cat from his own kitchen, he journeyed far across the moors until he reached a small green field. There he kindled a great fire, and when the fire was at its reddest he hung the cat over the blaze to roast it. There was no man there to witness the deed save the clansman, and he kept a sharp look-out for intruders.

But the unhappy cat let the world know of its plight, and in answer to its cries, all the cats in the Cameron country made haste to the spot. Ailean and his man were hard pressed to save their lives, but they succeeded in keeping the horde at bay, until a large black monster of a cat arrived and demanded an explanation.

Ailean nan Creach told the cat that by singeing the creature that hung over the fire he was atoning for his evil past. The giant cat spat contemptuously. ' Release my brother at once. There is another and a better way to make penance, Ailean nan Creach. For each of the forays you led as conqueror, see to it that a church is built to the glory of God.'

Ailean doubted the great cat, but he saw that if he

[1] *Ailean nan Creach*, Alan of the Forays

continued to roast the other, he and his man would be slain on the spot. 'I swear to build seven churches before I die,' he said at length, and released the howling creature by the fire.

Off went all the cats in a wild gallop, led by their still smouldering companion, and they never stopped until they reached the river Lochy. One after another they leapt into a pool. When they saw that Ailean's victim had quite recovered, they swam to the shore and made their way home.

Cameron kept his word. And when he died seven churches stood where no church had stood before, at Kill-a-choreill, Kildonan, Loch Leven, Kilmallie, Kilchoan, Kilkellen and Morven.

*

Nuair is mo a fhuair mi 'sann is lugha bha agam.
The more I got, the less I had.

18   THE TWO HUNCHBACKS

In the isle of Iona there lived a young man by the name of Fachie, who was kind, good-natured and helpful at all times. His skill in sailing a boat was known to everyone, and when the islanders gathered for the *ceilidhs* [1] on the winter nights there were few who could tell such wonderful stories. Yet Fachie was unhappy, with a secret sorrow always at his heart, for his body was bent and misshapen because of a great ugly hump that had grown upon his back.

Although it was in his nature always to be making light of his troubles, there were times when Fachie found it hard enough to smile. When his body ached as it often did, Fachie could bear the pain. But there

[1] *ceilidh*, fireside gathering during which the company joins in song and story-telling

54

were times, like when he met Cairistiona of the fair
hair, when it seemed to him that the lump on his back
was too hideous a thing to be borne. For he loved
the maiden dearly, although she had no more than
sympathy and understanding to offer the unhappy
young man.

When the black mood was on him, Fachie would
shun his fellows and seek out the loneliest parts of the
island. Sometimes he walked by the sea, by the white
sands, or stayed to watch the breakers curling under
the towering cliffs. But more often he climbed to the
summit of Dun-I, the hill to which the islanders
seldom came, and waited until the mood passed.

It was on such a day that Fachie left the village
and began his solitary climb up the gently sloping
hillside. As he passed, the crofters nodded to each
other understandingly. 'Fachie is finding his hump
heavy today,' they whispered. But they left him to
himself, and by and by poor Fachie cast himself down
on the green summit of Dun-I, to watch the red sun
go down into the sea.

He was still there when the moon came up. The
night wind began to whisper strange sounds in his
ears, helping him to forget his troubles. The moonlight, too, was playing strange tricks with his eyesight,
making giants' castles out of the boulders and
changing the shadows into the dancing shapes of
little men.

But as he lingered under the stars with his ear close
to the green turf, he heard sounds that the wind could
not make. It was a small singing voice that was
making a song out of two words—' Monday—Tuesday
—Monday—Tuesday.' The singer was not far off.
Indeed, it seemed as if he was just behind the nearest
boulder, so loud and clear was the song. Fachie
crawled forward and peeped round the rock, to see a

little man dancing round a clump of rushes. It was the strangest dance Fachie had ever seen. Round and round the little fellow would turn, until the song came to the word ' Tuesday,' and there he would be left hopping with his leg in the air. ' Och, och, och ! ' Fachie heard him complain in a shrill voice, ' what would I be giving to anyone who would help me find an end to the *port a beul* [1] ! For it is not much of a dance that leaves one with his leg high in the air ! '

When Fachie understood, he rolled over and chuckled. The little man was off again, singing his strange song and dancing his odd little dance to the tune. But as soon as the word ' Tuesday ' was reached, the little fellow stopped, and not one step farther could he go.

Now Fachie had an ear for music. He saw that one word more would end the song properly, and that word was ' Wednesday.' He waited till the little man tried again, and then he sang out the missing word— ' Wednesday ! ' Immediately the little man whooped with delight, for not only the song but the dance was now complete.

The fairy skipped over the grass and stood before Fachie. He took off his cap, bowed and thanked him. Then he asked how he might repay his skill and kindness. Fachie replied that he had need for nothing in this world.

' Indeed,' said the little man, ' then what brings you to the summit of Dun-I after sundown ? ' When Fachie told him of his one sorrow the fairy listened in silence. Then without a word he ran round the hillside and was gone, to return almost at once with a band of little men exactly like himself. Before Fachie had time to know what was happening the

[1] *port a beul*, literally ' music of the mouth ' to which dances were performed

56

little fellows were on his back. He felt their small hands tugging and tugging, until at last it seemed as if the cares of the world had been lifted from his shoulders. He stood up. His hump had gone! The fairies were dancing in a ring, in the middle of which lay the hideous hump!

Fachie thanked the little men and hurried home. For many days afterwards this wonder was talked of abroad, until it reached as far as the island of Tiree. There another misshapen man, with a hump like Fachie's, heard the story. But this man, whose name was Hugh, was as cruel and greedy as Fachie was kind and helpful. Indeed it was said that he was such a greedy rascal the housewives hid the hens' food until he had passed.

No sooner had Hugh the hunchback heard of Fachie's good fortune than he stole a neighbour's boat and set sail for Iona. Fachie told him where the fairy had danced on Dun-I, and Hugh hurried off to be there before midnight.

Now if Hugh had behaved himself I might have had another tale to tell you, but he didn't. He lay on the hill, waiting impatiently until the last glow of the sun had gone from the sky. Then, as before, the little man appeared. Hugh heard him sing his song, ' Monday — Tuesday — Wednesday — Monday — Tuesday—Wednesday,' while he performed his dance. Hugh knew that Fachie had helped to make the song the little man sang so merrily. So he decided he would put a twist to the melody himself. ' Thursday!' he screamed from his hiding-place.

The little man went on dancing, adding the new word to his tune. But now everything seemed topsy-turvy. The word didn't fit, and there he was, back to the beginning again, with his leg kicking high in the air! Hugh the hunchback rolled on the hillock

laughing at the little man. This made the fairy
angrier than ever. He looked to see who had spoiled
his tune and his dance for him. Hugh laughed louder
than ever, then he caught the little man by the leg.
'Before you go, *bodachan*, take this ugly hump I
have on my back and roll it down the hillside,' he
demanded.

58

' To do that,' replied the little man, ' I shall need my brothers.'

' Then fetch them this minute,' ordered Hugh. Whereupon the fairy ran off, to return with scores of others exactly like himself. They made a great ring round Hugh, ordering him to lie upon his face on the grass. ' Off with my hump! Off with my hump!' he cried impatiently. He felt the fairies on his shoulders, and urged them to make haste. At length he was told to rise. Hugh did as he was bid, but now it seemed as if the weight on his shoulders had been doubled. He could not stand upright. ' What is this you have done to me ? ' he screamed angrily.

' For your pains,' cried the little man, ' you have no longer one hump upon your back, but *two*.' And off they ran down the hillside. Hugh found that that was indeed the truth. Now he bore Fachie's as well as his own hump upon his back ! He was so ashamed, I can tell you, that he went to live in the farthest corner of Scotland where he stayed with his two humps until the end of his days. As for Fachie, he married Cairistiona, and for all I know his children's children are living in Iona to this day.

A' CHAILLEACH SA' BHROIG

(The old woman who lived in a shoe)

An cual' thu mu'n chaillich
Bha fuireach sa' bhroig ?
Bha 'n teaghlach cho lionmhor
Gun rian orr' no doigh.
Thug i dhaibh brochan
Gun aran, gun mharag ;
Is sgailc i gu cruaidh iad
'Gan ruagadh do'n leabaidh.

IT has been said that there is no finer castle in all
Scotland than that of Dunvegan in the isle of Skye.
It stands proudly on an eminence a little way from
the village of Dunvegan, and from its towers one can
gaze across tree-tops and blue waters to the hills of
Duirinish, Macleod's Tables, Healaval More and
Healaval Beg, southwards to the Coolins and east-
wards across brown rolling moors.

It is not surprising that many legends have been
woven round so impressive and beautiful a fortress
which, according to old tales, dates back to the tenth
century. But without doubt the best-known story is
told about the Fairy Flag. This relic is still to be
seen hanging in a glass case upon a castle wall. It is
no more than a faded scrap of cloth, yellow and
fragile with age, ready, it would seem, to crumble to
dust if touched by human hands.

The origin of the Fairy Flag must remain unknown.
One tale tells of a chieftain of the Macleods who
entered a fairy hill where he met a beautiful maiden.
He fell in love with her and begged her to be his wife.
The fairy maiden agreed on condition that he would
release her from mortal life at the end of twenty
years. They lived happily in the great castle until the
time came for Macleod's lady to return to fairyland.

One day as they stood on a little bridge near the
castle Macleod was dismayed to hear her remind him
of his promise. He loved her dearly, and the thought
of parting grieved him so much that he tried to hold
her back. But the call of Fairyland in her ears was
stronger even than the love she bore for her lord.
She escaped from his embrace, ran into the woods
before he could follow and was never seen again.

Macleod was left in sorrow with a scrap of her gown clutched in his hand, and this is said to be the fragment that remains in the glass case, the magic Fairy Flag of Dunvegan.

Another tale claims that the Flag is part of a cover that the fairies laid one day on an infant chieftain to preserve him from evil; while yet another relates its origin to a crusade undertaken by a chief to the Holy Land. There he encountered a she-devil who fought with him and left the hem of her dress in his fingers before she fled back to the underworld.

Whatever its origin the Flag was known to have supernatural properties. Three times could its possessors wave it to call for help in distress. It has been waved on two occasions. The first time an infant Macleod was at the point of death; the Flag was waved and the child recovered. The second time it was waved it rallied Macleod's men to victory in battle.

The Flag has yet to be waved for the last time. When that occasion arises it is doubtful if the fabric will do more than fall in dust. Meantime it remains for all to see, an interesting and awe-inspiring reminder of a promise given to the great chiefs of Macleod by the mysterious wee folk hundreds of years ago.

UAN BEAG MAIRI
(*Mary had a little lamb*)

Bha uan beag Mairi boidheach mear
'S a chloimh mar shneachd an t-sleibh;'
Is ge b'e ait 'n deidheadh Mairi bheag
Bha 'n t-uan a' ruith 'na deidh.

Aon la 's ann lean e i do'n sgoil,
Is bhris e 'n riaghailt chruaidh—
A 'chlann ag gaireachdaich 's ag cluich
Nuair chunnaic iad an t-uan.

20 DIARMAID AND THE WILD BOAR

No collection of Highland folk tales would be complete without mention being made of the Feine, a race of warriors whose ancestors were gods. Their hunting ground extended from the land of Erin to the wild mountains of Argyll, and tales of their deeds are almost without number.

The leader of this band was Fin MacCoul. Although he was gentle as the south wind, sweet-tongued and merry, he could terrify the bravest in battle with his strength and valour. This giant among men chose for his bride the beautiful Grainne, daughter of the High King of Ireland. Preparations for the wedding were duly made, and on the morning before the nuptials a great banquet was made ready for the guests.

It happened that Grainne found herself seated opposite a tall handsome young man, and she found her eyes drawn to him. He proved to be Diarmaid, nephew of Fin himself. But she did not know that the *searc*, or love-spot, on his cheek caused all women who saw it to lose their hearts to him exactly as she had done herself.

Before the feast was over Grainne begged the young man to flee with her into the forest. But Diarmaid refused. She was already betrothed to Fin his uncle. Grainne then put him under ' *greise* ' or bond no hero could refuse to honour, and at last persuaded Diarmaid to change his mind.

For many days they journeyed together through dense forests, living frugally on wild berries and animals Diarmaid hunted and killed. Soon word came to him that Fin was in pursuit with his followers. The day came when Diarmaid and Grainne had to hide in a hut, for Fin had at last tracked them down and was determined to kill them both. The hut was protected by a stout fence. Fin set his warriors to guard each side, then called upon Diarmaid to surrender. But Diarmaid had a foster-father with supernatural powers called Angus. On hearing the plight of his foster-child now grown to manhood he made haste to his aid. He urged both Grainne and Diarmaid to make their escape under cover of a cloak of invisibility which he had brought, but Diarmaid refused. Grainne, however, departed under its protection and followed Angus into the heart of the highest forest.

As soon as they had gone Diarmaid called the wind to his aid, and with a mighty leap flew over the heads of the waiting Feine. He reached the forest before Fin could collect his men, and made such speed that his pursuers were left far behind. But the chase was not yet over. Before the day was out Fin and his men were close enough for Diarmaid to hear their voices and the rattle of their swords. This time he chose for hiding a rowan-tree in the centre of a glade.

The Feine reached the roots of the tree, weary after the chase, and decided to rest there overnight. But the light still lingered. Fin challenged his son Fergus to play a game of chess. They played until only one move remained on the board, and that move would end the game with Fin master.

Diarmaid, hidden in the branches, had followed the play, and he alone saw the move. He plucked a berry from the rowan and dropped it on the chess-man. Fergus immediately saw the move and won the game.

Fin then challenged his second son Ossian to play. Once again the board was set. Fin played this time with even greater cunning, and as before one move was left to let him win. But Diarmaid plucked another berry. It fell on the chess-man to be moved. Once more Fin was defeated. Fin, however, was suspicious. No-one but Diarmiad of the love-spot could have matched such skill as he had shown and known which piece to move. He looked into the branches and called if Diarmaid was hidden there. No hero of the Feine was permitted to speak falsely, and Diarmaid was obliged to reply.

Diarmaid appeared before the assembled Feine. Fin would have slain him on the spot, but his companions prevailed upon him to forgive his kinsman. Fin agreed reluctantly. Diarmaid then joined Grainne and Angus, and within the span of the moon's journey across the heavens, Grainne and Diarmaid were wed. But Fin never forgave Diarmaid. Before long he persuaded Diarmaid to arm himself and hunt down a wild boar that roamed the hills. The creature had escaped death at the hands of the Feine many times, yet a hero there must be valiant enough to bring about its destruction.

Diarmaid accepted Fin's challenge. The wild boar broke from its hiding-place, but before it could strike with its formidable tusks Diarmaid's spear had reached its heart. Fin pretended to be well pleased. He invited Diarmaid to pace the creature's length as it lay on the grass. ' I am not satisfied, Diarmaid ! ' he cried when the hero had measured twenty foot lengths from head to tail. ' Let it be measured again ! '

This time Diarmaid paced out the length of the carcase from tail to head, against the lie of the bristles. In doing so a bristle on the spine pierced his heel. Diarmaid gave a great cry and fell mortally hurt, for the bristle had entered the one vulnerable spot in all his body.

There was yet time to save his life. He called to Fin to bring him a draught of water in his cupped hands. Not even Fin could harden his heart and refuse the wish. He filled his hands at a spring, and was on the point of kneeling before the fallen Diarmaid when he remembered the treachery of the faithless Grainne and the determination of Diarmaid to make her his own wife. The water spilled into the grass, and with a last salute to his old comrades Diarmaid turned away his face and died.

SIMON SIMPLIDH
(Simple Simon)

Simon Simplidh 's Rob nam Bonnach
A 'dol thun na feille ;
Thuirt Simon Simplidh, ' Roib, a bhalaich,
Reic iad sin rium fein.'

Thuirt Rob nam Bonnach, ' Ceart a tha thu ;
Cait a bheil do sgillin ? '
Thuirt Simon Simplidh, ' Siud mo phocaid !
Faic thu, cha' eil gin innt'. '

Simon Simplidh chaidh e dh' iasgach
Null gu ceann na bathaich,
'N duil gun glacadh e muc-mhara
' N cuinneag uisg ' a mhathar.

21 A ROMANCE OF LOCH LEVEN

CAMERON, laird of Callart, lived in a big old house close to the shores of Loch Leven. Mairi his daughter was young and fair. She numbered amongst her friends many of the humble folk in the neighbourhood, and her father, a proud man, disapproved of her associating with them.

One day he saw her talking to a lad from Ballachulish. As punishment she was forbidden to see anyone for a month, her father making sure she would not disobey his order by locking her in her own room. During her imprisonment a trading ship arrived in Loch Leven, bringing fine silks, satin and gewgaws for all to buy. The household of Callart were amongst the first to visit the ship. Mairi in her room waited for their return. They brought with them fineries to delight any maiden's heart, but Mairi was obliged to listen behind the locked door while they discussed and admired their purchases.

Next morning, however, a great stillness had fallen on the house. Neither foot nor voices sounded in the hall nor on the stairs. Mairi could not understand why no-one answered her calls, until at midday villagers arrived in the courtyard. She raised her window to see the lad from Ballachulish in the midst of the crowd. He called to her that the ship had brought the ' black plague ' with it, that all in Callart House were either dead or doomed, and that he had orders to burn the house and all within lest the plague spread farther.

Mairi pleaded with him to postpone the burning until word had been taken to Diarmid her lover at Inverawe. Her wish was granted. Diarmid came in the night. He slipped past the guards, who had been posted to prevent contact being made with anyone who still lived within the plague-stricken walls, and threw a stout rope to the waiting girl. Mairi made it fast and descended to safety. Diarmid then told her to cleanse herself thoroughly in the waters of a nearby burn before dressing herself in fresh clothes he had brought for the purpose. By the time dawn was breaking she was with her lover and watching the torches lighted and the great house in flames.

The couple made their way to Loch Awe and Diarmid's ancestral home. But they were forbidden to cross the threshold. Campbell of Inverawe,

Diarmid's father, appeared at a high window. He ordered them to stand together, hand in hand, and pronounced them man and wife. Then to make certain they had not been smitten with the scourge nor were able to contaminate anyone by contact, he made them vow they would seek the solitude of a bothy in the heights of Ben Cruachan and remain there alone for forty days.

It was a strange honeymoon following on a stranger marriage. Diarmid and Mairi did as they were bid and lived happily for the rest of their lives together. When Diarmid died of wounds in the battle of Inverlochy years afterwards, a bard of the Camerons put into song the love that Mairi Cameron of Callart had for her fallen lover.

22 THE ' FORTY-FIVE '

OF all the famous and historic personalities that have emerged from the history of the Scottish Highlands, that of Charles Edward Stuart, son of James, Pretender to the throne of Scotland, is perhaps the most colourful.

Born in exile on the Continent, the Prince needed only the persuasion of Irish exiles like Sir Thomas Sheridan and Scots advisers like Murray of Broughton to tempt him to sail to Scotland and make a bold bid for the Scottish Crown.

He came in the summer of 1745 on a little ship, the *Doutelle*, after a skirmish in the Channel with an English warship during which the *Elizabeth*, a companion vessel, was hard hit and returned to harbour. MacDonald of Boisdale met him on the island of Eriskay where the Prince first landed.

' Go home,' advised the chief who was doubtful of the wisdom of the enterprise.

' I am come home, sir,' replied the young adventurer, and continued his voyage, to land with seven trusted followers at Moidart.

At first it seemed that MacDonald's advice had been wise. The clan chiefs received him with uncertainty, afraid to commit themselves to so uncertain a venture. Even Cameron of Lochiel held back, but in the end he came under the spell of the eager young man who had set his hopes on attaining success. Lochiel and his seven hundred clansmen accompanied Charles to Glen Finnan, where the Standard was raised.

From then on success seemed assured. The clans rallied, the Jacobite army began to grow in strength, until Lord George, Earl of Murray, the Prince's aide-de-camp, commanded a force of two thousand five hundred men and marched to the capital.

Sir John Cope, who was in command of the regular army, made a half-hearted attempt to intercept the rebels, then turned tail for Inverness. The road to Edinburgh was open, and in a few days Charles had entered the city, opposition having been easily overcome. The heralds raised their trumpets. James VIII was proclaimed king at the Mercat Cross.

Cope returned and approached Edinburgh from the east. With the army at the gates Charles gathered his men and prepared to join battle. After a brilliant charge Cope's men were put to flight by the Highlanders, and he himself escaped to carry the news of his own sorry rout to Berwick.

Had Charles shown wisdom and followed up his first successes by marching straightway into England, history might have read differently today. But he tarried in the city to celebrate his good fortune. From then on disaster followed on the heels of defeat, until the Jacobite army that had marched so proudly across the border, almost to the walls of London, was in the end destroyed and disbanded on Culloden Moor.

Charles retreated to the island of North Uist where he had counted on boarding a ship for France. But the island was well-nigh overrun with soldiers and he himself carried a price of £30,000 pounds on his head.

It is to the credit of the islanders that no-one sought to reveal his presence. Eventually a lady, Flora MacDonald, came to his rescue. She obtained a permit to land in Skye with her maid ' Betty Burke.' The Prince disguised himself in woman's clothes, assumed the name and identity of Flora's maid, and after a perilous journey reached the romantic misty isle.

Alas, it was only to discover that Skye, like North Uist, was a place of danger. He reached the mainland and concealed himself in a cave with seven known robbers as companions. From thence he made his way over the mountains to Ben Aldur. This time his hiding-place was ' Cluny's Cage,' a rude hut built of sticks hidden in the trees on the mountain-side, where Cluny himself and Cameron of Lochiel kept his whereabouts unknown for many days.

Not until September in the year 1746, five long months after Culloden, did he manage to make his way to a ship. He sailed from Scotland, never to return, and died an inglorious death in squalor in 1788.

With his departure came a time of sorrow and humiliation for the Highlands. The clan system was destroyed, rights and privileges taken away, and even the tartan which the clans loved so dearly was forbidden as a dress. But the memory of the Young Pretender who had come so near to wearing the Scottish crown, and who had endeared himself to rich and poor alike with his ready laugh and charm of manner, continued to live long after the last bitter defeat of a lost cause.

PEIGI BHEAG A SUARDAIL
(*Little Polly Flinders*)

Peigi bheag a Suadrail
Shuidh i anns an luathadh,
'S ghar i casan beag sa' ghriosach.
Thainig oirre mathair
Is thug i dhi na straicean
Mar shalaich i cuid aodaich cho riasaich.

23 THE LUCKY HORSESHOE

IAIN, the black-bearded smith and farrier of Taynuilt, put his head out of the smiddy door to see who rode so hard and so fast along the dusty road. Great was his astonishment to see a giant horse, approaching riderless in a cloud of dust. He stood aside in time to let the creature enter the door, waited until it settled, then made a careful approach to catch the bridle.

'Make haste, make haste, blacksmith!' cried the horse in a loud voice. 'I have need of four stout shoes. Already it is past mid-day, and my journey is still to finish.' The smith saw at once that he had none other than the Devil himself in his smiddy. Moreover the demon was sore distressed, with fetlocks streaked with blood, and hooves that had suffered in the ruts and rubble of the roadways. Iain resolved he would pay dearly for his evil and misdeeds!

After examining the beast's hooves he addressed the creature. 'I have shoes to fit. But first I must pare the soles. See that you stand quietly.' Thereupon the farrier set the shoes to heat, and began to clean each broken hoof. Presently he was ready to

70

set the shoes and nail them tight. But by then the demon horse was squealing and dancing with pain.

'Stop, stop, man!' he cried, trying hard to escape. But the farrier held him firmly, and proceeded with his work. The beast plunged and reared in agony. 'Make your terms, blacksmith! Anything that is in my power I will do, but mercy, I beg of you! Mercy!'

The blacksmith chuckled in his beard, for he knew that he had the Devil in his power.

'Very well,' he replied. 'But let us strike a bargain. Wherever a horseshoe hangs upon a door or lintel, let the place within be sanctuary from all evil, from witch or warlock, or from the Unclean Beast himself. Say ye so, horse-without-rider, and you shall be shod without further pain.'

The demon horse was so anxious to be gone and free of further pain at the hands of the righteous blacksmith, that it promised to respect the sign of the horseshoe. And today the doors are many which bear the charm that wards off the powers of darkness and the Evil Eye.

*

Uis, uis, air an each,
Nighean phapaidh air an each.
C'a ruigidh sinn an nochd,
Ruigidh sinn a bha laidh.

[*The foregoing might be sung by a lass riding home on her father's back, just as a little girl under similar circumstances in England would sing 'Ride-a-cock-horse.'*]

*

Socraichidh am posadh an gaol.
Love is soon cooled by marriage.

MAGGIE, the lass that John More, the Perthshire farmer, chose to marry, was as pretty and slim as John was big and burly. John was congratulated on his good fortune for Maggie had been—and still was —the beauty of the parish.

He was very proud of his small attractive wife, but there was only one thing he had cause to regret. She had a lusty voice that was as deep as a bell, and when she spoke overlong John fidgeted. As the days passed Maggie's voice irritated her husband so much that he could not sit to listen. He would go out and leave her, to wander by the burn and nurse his misfortune.

One night as Maggie sat by the fire talking, John snatched up his hat and stumped out. He reached the burn and stood looking into the water.

' Man, oh, man,' he said glumly to himself, ' what wouldn't I give for a wife without a tongue ! '

' Give me the strength of your arms,' cried a voice, ' and I'll whisk it out by the roots ! '

' I won't say " no " to that ! ' declared John to a brownie who was struggling to shift a boulder by the bank.

' Then roll this stone into the water, for my house is flooded ! ' cried the brownie breathlessly.

John More gave the boulder a heave. It rolled into the water with a splash, turning the flow of water into a new channel, so that the old bed of the burn became dry.

' Now home with you, John More,' said the brownie. ' Your wife will be henceforth as dumb as those that sleep in the kirkyard.'

John went home to find his wife in a fury. Sure

enough not an inch of tongue was left in her head, and not a word could she utter. If poor Maggie was miserable, John More was delighted, and that night he laughed himself to sleep, while Maggie wept for her lost tongue.

A year passed and then Maggie began to grow fat. She steadily increased in size until she was as round as a butter ball. The day arrived when she had grown too stout to work about the house, and the kitchen seemed so small that once again John More was obliged to go outside. He decided to search for the brownie one night when the moon was full, and great was his relief when he saw the little man on the green bank.

' I have a wife without a tongue, but she has grown so fat I can scarcely turn in my own kitchen. The hearth is piled with cinders. There is dirt in every corner. And I am miserable for want of the food she is too fat to cook in the pot.'

' Sad I am to hear it, John More, but you had your wish. There's naught I can do to comfort you this day,' replied the fairy.

John More coaxed and pleaded but the brownie had nothing to offer him. ' Then,' stormed John in a rage, ' it's the burn that will go back into your kitchen,' and he leapt into the water, seized the stone and heaved it back on the bank. The current immediately swirled back to flow in its old bed again.

The brownie began to dance with rage. ' Take the chatter of the burn with you, John More,' he squealed. ' And long life to both of you for flooding my house ! '

John More laughed at the brownie's problem. But when he reached home he soon found out the meaning of the little man's words. Maggie his wife was filling the doorway. The tongue was in her head once more, and her voice was no longer deep but shrill as the sound of the burn flowing over pebbles. From that day and for many long years Maggie nagged and scolded her husband as steadily as the flood of water that had filled the brownie's kitchen; and it cannot be said that he did not deserve it!

MAIRI AIR STOL
(*Little Miss Muffet*)

Mairi air stol
Ag itheadh 's ag ol
Meag 's bainne-bhinid air leth;
Shuidh damhan-allaidh
Ri taobh 's e 'ga h-amharc,
'S ruith Mairi le eagal a beath'.

*

Theid a t-anfhann dichiollach thar an laidir leisg.
The diligent weak will triumph over the lazy strong.

25 THE MAGIC CHURN

LACHIE was nine years of age. He was perhaps small for his age, but there was the strength and suppleness of the willow in his body. And certainly he could run faster than any other boy in the glen, faster even than Duncan his stepbrother, who was fully a year older. This did not please Duncan at all, who was big and rough, and who liked nothing better than to tease Lachie whenever it was possible.

Duncan it was who was sent with the cattle to the shieling, while small Lachie stayed at home to work at the croft. Lachie envied Duncan his days on the hillside in the summer air, for he had nothing more to do than see that the cattle did not stray from the pastures.

One day when Lachie was drawing water from the well he heard someone weeping near by. He peeped behind the dyke to see a little man buried under a heap of peats that had fallen from the stack. Lachie scrambled over the dyke, pulled aside the peats and helped the little man to his feet.

By this time Lachie was a little bit afraid, for by the green colour of his coat, and the pointed cap and shoes, he saw that this was no mortal but one of the wee folk who lived in the hills. Indeed he would have run off had not the little man caught him by the sleeve.

' Tell me, Lachie,' said he, ' what keeps you here at the croft while Duncan is off at the shieling with the cattle ? '

' Today,' replied Lachie, ' I have to draw water to clean the milking pails ; then I have to help make the butter.'

' I can make butter too,' said the little man in green, ' the sweetest butter that ever you tasted. Let me see your *muigh*[1] and I will teach you how it is done.'

Lachie showed the little man the butter-churn. It was large and heavy, so heavy indeed that Lachie was quite sure the little fellow would not be able to move it one little bit. But the little man made no attempt to lay his hand on it. He sat on a milking stool and began to sing a strange song that Lachie had never heard before. As he sang he rocked to and fro. Meanwhile the basin of cream began to slip from the shelf, tilted slowly and poured the cream smoothly into the churn so that not a drop was spilled.

Next the churn began to rock to the rhythm of the *port a beul*.[2] It began gently at first but soon it was dancing merrily round about, while the cream

[1] *muigh*, a churn   [2] *port a beul*, mouth-music

splashed and slopped inside. In no time the butter was ready. The fairy hopped from the stool, bowed to the bewitched butter-churn and, naming the Five Sisters—which were mountains in Kintail—from east to west, begged it to stop.

Lachie watched with wondering eyes as the little man separated the butter and laid it out in little pats for him to taste. It was as he had promised—the sweetest butter that Lachie had ever tasted !

When Lachie turned to thank the fairy he found that he had vanished. At that moment his parents appeared. When they saw the yellow butter they were astonished. But when they found that it tasted as no other butter had ever tasted they could find no words to praise Lachie for his skill.

From that day Lachie was left to make the butter. The neighbours heard of it, and they too declared that Lachie's butter was the finest in the land. Very soon they came from far and near to buy Lachie's butter until the money in the house overfilled the purses.

But not a word did Lachie say about the *bodachan* [1] and the secret of the churn.

Duncan, as you can imagine, was not pleased with this at all. He grew more jealous of his stepbrother as the days passed. When he demanded to know how Lachie did it the little boy ran off. And as Duncan was slow of foot he could never catch him.

One day he decided to find out the secret for himself. He rose very early in the morning and hid behind a wooden chest. When Lachie came to make the butter he listened very carefully. Lachie sat on the milking stool as the fairy had done and began to sing. Immediately the cream was emptied into the churn, the churn began to dance merrily by itself on the flagstones. By and by, when the butter was ready,

---

[1] *bodachan*, little old man

Lachie bowed as the fairy had done and, naming the Five Sisters of Kintail from east to west, he begged the churn to stop. When Duncan saw Lachie lay the golden butter pats in rows upon the shelf he chuckled to himself. 'Now I have the secret. I will make butter too—sweeter perhaps than Lachie's.'

The days passed and soon there was enough cream in the basins to be made into butter. Duncan rose again long before the others were awake. He sat himself on the milking stool and began to sing the song he had heard Lachie sing. Obediently the cream flowed from the basins into the churn. The churn itself began to rock and spin and dance merrily before him. Duncan clapped his hands with delight.

By and by the butter began to appear at the mouth of the dancing churn. Duncan tasted it. It was as sweet as ever. But the rascal was not only sly but greedy. He kept the churn dancing until the butter spilled over. 'I will make butter enough to sell the length and breadth of Kintail,' he told himself, 'then I will be the richest man in Scotland.'

The foolish boy collected the golden pats in basins and in trays. He let it spill on the floor, scraping it together in heaps. The time came when he decided he had made sufficient, then he tried to stop the churn, as Lachie had done, by bowing and naming the Five Sisters. Alas, he had forgotten the order of the names!

Meanwhile the butter came pouring from the churn in a stream that would not be stopped. It rose about him in heaps, waist high, until he could not move. 'Stop! Stop!' he screamed when the wretched stuff touched his chin, afraid now that his greed would cost him his life.

The noise woke Lachie and his parents. They ran to the kitchen to find it filled with butter, the churn still dancing merrily round, and Duncan almost completely hidden. Lachie bowed and whispered the magic words, and the churn stopped at once.

It was midday before they succeeded in digging Duncan out of the yellow mountain. And it was sunset before the last of the butter had been swept from the house. Duncan was beaten for his pains, but the spell had been broken. The churn was no longer bewitched. No more would it dance merrily as it churned out butter.

Lachie was very sad, but from that day it was Duncan who was put to the churning, while Lachie went off on the fine summer days to herd the cattle at the shielings !

*

Cha robh Samhradh riamh gun ghrian ;
Cha robh Geamhradh riamh gun sneachd.

There never was a Summer without sun ;
There never was Winter without snow.

26 A LEGEND OF THE BIRDS

YEARS ago when the world was young, there lived two giants, and they were mortal enemies.

Geamhradh, as cruel and ugly as Samhradh was gentle and good to look upon, lived in a cave hollowed out of a mountain of ice. There, in darkness, he slept for half the year, shaking the world with the sound of his snoring.

Meanwhile Samhradh had come from his sunny kingdom in the south. And with his coming the earth turned over and woke. The sun smiled upon the flocks in the field. The woodlands, green with fresh foliage, were filled with the songs of birds. Wild creatures met him unafraid, and where his foot had trodden flowers bloomed and gave forth their sweetest perfumes.

But each year the day came when Geamhradh returned. First a black scowl of cloud appeared. The wind grew colder, until at last the giant's ugly head appeared above the mountain-tops. He flung the snow before him. His frosty breath stripped the trees of every leaf and hardened the earth.

Samhradh hated to see the earth shiver and watch the birds fly southwards. But he loved peace and would not fight his enemy. His rule would last only a little while, and the sun would shine again.

One day the gentle Samhradh was asleep beneath a tree when Geamhradh crawled out of his cave. Finding his enemy unprepared, he tore a great rock from the earth, and would have killed the sleeping giant had not the blackbird in the tree screamed a warning. Samhradh sprang aside, and the mighty boulder fell far beyond the mountains. To this day it remains far out in the Atlantic Ocean, the lonely island of St Kilda.

Then Geamhradh and Samhradh faced each other and began to fight. Geamhradh, fresh and strong after his long sleep, struck hard at the gentle Samhradh. Snow fell and a great storm raged about them. But Samhradh melted the snow as fast as it fell, until the rivers filled and spread in floods across the land.

Then the cunning Geamhradh breathed upon the water, so that many birds fell dead upon the shores, flocks perished in the fields, and even the edges of the sea was frozen. Samhradh stumbled, and as he fell, Geamradh dealt him a mighty blow. The fight that had lasted many days was over.

After Geamhradh had gone, two little birds in search

of food found the wounded giant in the snow. One was a robin and the other a wren.

' *Rud-eigin*,[1] ' whispered the wren in sorrow. ' The giant Samhradh is dead ! '

' Dying he may be, Jenny Wren,' replied the robin, ' but dead he is not yet.'

' Then we must save his life ! I will keep his heart warm while you find the fire that will bring him back into the world.' And the little Jenny Wren fluffed out her feathers, and spread her wings upon the giant's breast.

Robin searched far and wide for the fire that would save the giant Samhradh. He flew through the silent woods until he was tired and hungry. By and by he reached a lonely cottage at the edge of a forest. There was one window, and through it Robin saw a fire burning in the hearth.

Robin found a hole in the thatch upon the roof. He squeezed himself through, reached the hearth and lifted a small red cinder in his beak. Then he returned to where the giant lay. The cinder set a sprig of whin alight, and when the flame grew big enough Robin gathered branches and built a fire close to the giant.

When the warmth reached him, Samhradh stirred. Jenny Wren helped Robin to build the fire into a great blaze. At last Samhradh turned his head, blessed the little birds, and walked southwards to his kingdom where the sun would heal his wounds.

But after he had gone Robin crept under a bush. He put his head under his wing. The feathers were burnt from his breast, and he could no longer fly. For many days Jenny Wren wept for her mate. But Robin did not die. And when he crept from his hidey-hole his feathers had grown again, this time bright red where the fire had burned.

[1] *Rud-eigin*, Robin Redbreast

To this day the robin leaves his nest with a brown speckled breast, but the feathers that the fire burned never fail to turn red before winter comes.

IAIN BEAG NAN ADHAIRCEAN
(*Little Jack Horner*)

Iain Beag nan adhaircean
'Na shuidhe sa' chuil-mhonadh,
'G itheadh marag mhor na Nollaig,
Stob e steach innt' ordag,
'S thuirt e nuair sin,
' Bu mhi am balach ;
Chan 'eil ann cho coir rium ! '

*

' Tha biadh is ceol an so ! ' mar a thuirt am madadh ruadh,
'S e ruith air falbh leis a phiob.

' Here's both meat and music ! ' as the fox said, when it ran away with the bagpipes.

27 THE CHANGELING

SANDY M'OMISH was a tailor, and a very good tailor he was too. He lived near Scourie in Sutherlandshire, but it was seldom he stitched at his own fireside. For in those days it was the custom for the tailor to go to his customers, taking with him shears, cloth, needle and thread in a pack on his back.

Wherever he chanced to go there was a welcome for Sandy. It seemed that no sooner had he crossed the threshold than ill luck was whisked up the chimney. He seldom stayed for less than three days, stitching and gossiping cheerfully until the needs of the household were satisfied. Then he would be off again down the road to the next house, in search of more work at the next croft or *clachan*.[1]

One day Sandy was on his way to the back door of a cottage. He had just turned off the highroad and was about to open the gate, when he saw someone was already on the doorstep. The cottage was a lonely one. Indeed the next house was five miles and a bit farther on. He was surprised to see that the visitor was a *cailleach* [2] who was as bent as the *cromag* [3] she carried. Unlike the *cailleachs* of the north, who were dressed in sober grey or black, she wore a gown of the brightest green.

Just as the gate clicked shut behind the little tailor she turned quickly and looked at him. He saw as ugly a hag as ever he had seen, and the look she gave him reminded him of that of a weasel peeping from the stones of a dyke. Then a strange thing happened. Just when Sandy was wondering what to do next, the strange visitor skipped into the shadows and disappeared.

Sandy had a good look round about before he went to knock at the door, but there wasn't a sign of the old woman anywhere. He put down his pack on the step, and was on the point of rattling the latch, when the door began to open stealthily. Two hands reached out and handed him a bundle of clothes. Then, as mysteriously as it had opened, the door shut in his face.

To his surprise the bundle began to squirm. He undid the folds to find that he was holding an infant.

'God bless the house!' he whispered, 'but here is the strange thing! A *cailleach* there was on this threshold not two minutes ago, but she went off like a dried leaf on the wind! And now it is a child I am

[1] *clachan*, a village   [2] *cailleach*, an old woman
[3] *cromag*, a stick

holding that I have never seen before. I wonder if the fairies are in it ! Maybe I had better take this one home with me lest there is black witchery abroad.'

When Sandy reached home he told his wife what had happened, and she could understand it no better than her husband. But she agreed he had better go back to the cottage, and meantime leave the child in her care. Sandy therefore hurried back to the cottage, and found the crofter and his wife by the side of a cot, and the poor woman weeping bitterly.

' There has been no peace within this house this day ! ' he was told. ' This child of ours has suddenly become possessed of the devil, for he does nothing but scream like the black gulls on the shore ! '

No sooner had the woman spoken than the child began to screech and howl loud enough to lift the rafters, until Sandy persuaded the unhappy parents to go to bed and rest, promising that he would try to soothe the child while they slept. They agreed to do as he wished. Then the tailor loosened the child's clothing—and it was all he could do to keep from running from the house. For instead of a helpless infant, what he saw was a shrivelled creature with the prick-ears of a fox.

It was exactly as he had feared. The fairies had exchanged the human child for one of their own !

' There now, small one,' said the little tailor gently, ' what can I give ye ? '

' My ain mither ! ' cried the changeling, sitting up in the cot.

' Indeed and I might do that,' agreed Sandy. ' But first ye must tell me how am I to fetch her ? '

' Set me on my ain two feet, tailor-man. It's myself that can do the fetching ! '

Sandy lifted the manikin and set him on the table, where he began to hop, skip and scamper amongst the

teacups and dishes like the *maigheach* [1] in March moonlight. Then he caught the end of his long tail, put it in his mouth and began to finger it like a pipe chanter. To Sandy's horror and amazement the kitchen was suddenly filled with strange music that set the dogs outside howling dolefully.

'She is coming! She is coming!' skirled the piper in his thin voice, putting an end to the music, and looking towards the door.

Sandy waited with his tongue suddenly dry and his hair on end. A great gust of wind suddenly blew the fire out on the hearth and flung the door wide. In an instant the demon piper had leapt from the table and was gone.

'My bairn!' cried the crofter's wife, who had been roused by the awful din. 'What have ye done with my bairn, Sandy M'Omish!'

[1] *maigheach*, a hare

' I've done the best I could, good wife,' Sandy gasped as he sat on a chair. ' But if ye give me leave to find my breath again, I'll bring him back, safe and sound, to his own mother ! '

The little tailor at once went home and fetched the child back as he promised, none the worse for its adventure.

Sandy the tailor had never lacked friends and a warm welcome wherever he had gone. But from that day there were none who loved him as did the Scourie crofter and his wife, whose son he had rescued from the fairies.

*

Trian a thig gun iarraidh—eagal, iadach, is gaol.

Three things that come unbidden—fear, jealousy and love.

28 THE WITCH OF MAR

CAITIR FHRANAGACH was a small stooped woman. She was so old that no-one knew her age. And she lived alone in a small dark hovel not far from the castle of Abergeldie.

That she had the powers of evil and witchcraft was beyond dispute. She could bring the storm across the hills in the twinkling of an eye. She could fill the burns in yellow spate when no rain had fallen. Wherever a cow fell sick and died you could be sure Caitir Fhranagach had a hand in it. Few were willing to cross her path or pass within sight of her cottage lest they should come under her spell. The very sight of her crooked form on the road was enough to send the children running back to their homes.

The Caitir had lived so long apart from the rest of the community that she had come to expect neither

kindness nor a word of comfort from any quarter,
least of all from the Laird of Abergeldie or his fine
lady. It came therefore as a surprise when one day
the lady crossed her threshold and entered the crone's
kitchen.

The Caitir was spinning at the fireside, in the
company of a great yellow cat. 'What can the wife
of Abergeldie want with Caitir Fhranagach?' she
asked without looking up.

'I have come for help,' replied the lady. 'Let me

look into the future, *cailleach*, and the gold I have brought in this purse will be laid in your lap.'

'What is it you would see?' asked the Caitir in a voice that was hoarse as the croaking of the raven.

'I would see my own wedded lord. It is said that he has grown tired of me, and has chosen another. Tell me if the tale be true, and let me look upon the woman he brings from France to live at Abergeldie in my stead.'

The witch heard the chink of gold in the lady's purse, and nodded. She hirpled slowly to stir the fire, then filling a black pot with water, she set it to boil. Into it she sifted ashes, the stalks of plants and a white dust made from the skin of toads. In a little while the pot began to bubble. The steam began to curl up the chimney, and the Caitir drew her creepie close to the flames, rocking slowly to and fro, and murmuring words that were meaningless to the lady waiting by her side.

Presently the steam from the brew began to fill the kitchen like a blue mist. Strange shapes came and went, then a ship appeared out of the vapours. The bright sun shone on its sheets and on the men that moved across its deck. A little apart from the rest stood a tall man and a lady in a crimson gown, at the sight of which the wife of Abergeldie cried out in a sudden fury.

'It is true! Your witch's brew has revealed to me the evil of Gordon. Oh, that you could banish the sun, and raise a storm that would wreck the accursed ship and drown so false a husband!' She flung the purse of gold to the witch, who watched the golden coins spilling across the earth floor. 'Tell me,' she pleaded, 'it can be done, and I will fill the purse again twice over!'

'Lead me to Abergeldie keep, lady,' replied the witch.' There I can weave a spell to please you.'

The lady made haste with the Caitir Fhranagach, and they reached the castle. The witch slowly climbed a narrow winding stair that ended in a forgotten garret at the top of the highest turret. There she seated herself and ordered that a basin of water be carried to her. A servant brought the basin and set it before the witch. Next she asked the servant to fetch a shallow *cuach*.[1] When this was laid in her hands, she waited until the water became still before floating it in the centre.

She rose and asked that the lady sit where she herself had sat, to watch the *cuach* while she returned by the stairway. At the bottom of the stair lay the dungeon cell, and there the Caitir crawled into the darkest corner. The servant who listened heard the muttering and keening of the crone, trembling as the horrid sounds rose and fell, while in the garret the lady waited and watched as she was bid.

The water in the basin began to tremble. The *cuach* danced gently on the ripples. Slowly the ripples changed into little waves that leapt upwards, tossing the little craft to and fro. The water hissed and bubbled and splashed over, while the *cuach* rocked and turned over like a ship caught in a storm. When it seemed that the basin must topple over, a great wave leapt up to fill the *cuach* and sent it to the bottom.

The Caitir Fhranagach met the lady in the courtyard. 'It is as you wished, my lady. Abergeldie will never return.'

In the days that followed, the wife of Abergeldie was almost distracted. What the witch had claimed to have done had brought a change of heart. She

---

[1] *cuach*, a drinking-cup

prayed hourly for her husband and wished for his safe
return. But a messenger reached the castle before a
week was out with the news that the ship had indeed
foundered during a great storm, and all aboard had
perished.

Mad with grief the Lady of Abergeldie sent her men
to the witch's hovel to put her to death immediately.
But the Caitir saw them coming. They closed about
the house, broke open the door and entered. But
the witch had vanished. All that they saw was her
yellow cat in the company of another—a lean black
creature, that fled through the open door and disappeared in the nearby woods.

A fire was kindled in the thatch, and the cottage was
burned to the ground. But the witch had outwitted
them, for as the rafters crackled and the flames split
the roof-tree, Abergeldie's men heard the Caitir
Fhranagach mocking them from the depths of the
trees, in the thin wailing voice of a cat.

29 THE ROBBER-BARON AND THE MICE

WITHIN a few miles of the town of Inverness there is
said to be a green mound where countless mice have
their small homes. Many hundreds of years ago a
stout fortress stood on the mound, in which a robber-
baron lived with his band. This robber was so cruel
and fearsome of aspect that only the boldest would
venture near the valley in which the fortress was
hidden. Not only did the rogue terrorise the neighbourhood, but his raids led him far afield to steal the
good folks' herds, empty their purses and burn the
roofs of their houses over their heads.

That such a state of affairs should have been
tolerated in a land where clans were strong seems

strange. But the baron had built his fortress well.
The walls were thrice three feet in thickness everywhere ; there were no windows save three narrow
loopholes high up on the walls through which a sparrow
could scarcely have squeezed ; as for the solitary door
it was so little that a small man had to stoop to enter,
yet its oak timbers were sufficient to withstand the
fiercest blows of a battering-ram.

The time came when it was decided something
would have to be done to rid the neighbourhood of the
marauder. One day the clansmen assembled to march
against the common enemy. Unfortunately the baron
heard of their coming and had time to retire into his
fortress and close the door.

For seven days the army stormed the massive walls
and thrust against the door with *cabers* [1] cut in the
forests. But the robber laughed at their vain efforts.
Then a young chief from the hills came forward with
a plan. He set all the *cailleachs* to spin from morning
until night until they had prepared as many yards of
thread as there are mountains in Scotland. He sent
his clansmen to trap as many mice as could be found
under the meal-chests and bring them to him alive.
Then, under cover of darkness, he crawled with the
captured mice to the robber's castle, fastened to each
a thread smeared with tallow, and set them free at the
door.

The mice scurried through a hole between the
timbers, each score of mice taking with it a like
number of threads. Very soon the threads became
crossed and twisted until they formed a net. The net
became a rope laid along the corridors of the fortress.
Outside in the darkness the young chief put a light to
the ends of the threads. The fire crept along each
thread, through the chink in the door and began to

---

[1] *cabers*, trunks of trees stripped of branches

burn fiercely inside as the rope thickened. First a stool caught alight, then a table, until in the end the rafters were burning.

By then the robbers were roused out of their sleep and saw how they had been tricked. It was a case of surrendering to the army who waited outside or remaining to be roasted alive. They made a determined attempt to escape, but after a brief encounter, they were beaten and disarmed and thrown into prison.

History does not tell the nature of their punishment. It is said that the young chieftain lived to lead many armies to victory in the years of his life. But he is best remembered by his clever trick by which he humbled a ruthless reiver by means of an army of little brown mice.

HEIGH-DIDDLE-DIDDLE

(Hey-diddle-diddle)

' Mo chreach ! ' ars a' phiseag,
An cat ag cluich an fhidhill,
'S leum a' bho thar na gealaich le ran ;
Lach an cu beag
Ris an spors a bha siud,
'S ruith an truinnsear air falbh leis an spain.

30 ANGUS OG AND THE BIRDS

THOSE who have lived in the north of Scotland will know how long the daylight lingers during the months of summer. Sometimes it seems that the golden afterglow of sunset will last until the coming of the next dawn, and there will be no night at all.

But a time there must be for sleep, and that comes

when a great hush falls upon the earth one hour before daybreak.

Many hundreds of years ago, so the legend says, there was no end to the day. Time for sleep was hard to find, for always, day and night, birds would be restless on the moors and in the woodlands, keeping their neighbours awake with their endless singing.

Angus Og, the god of Spring, listened to the voices of the birds, and they displeased him. He could not banish the light, but he decided he must put such a weariness upon the sleepless ones that they would be glad to rest. And this is how it was done.

He summoned all the birds from the moors, the mountains and the glens, and when they were gathered about him on a green knoll, he asked which of them was the loudest singer. At that there was a fierce argument, for none could agree.

' Very well,' said the young god, ' from daybreak tomorrow all of you will sing. I will sit on Ben Cruachan, and the voice I hear singing above all others will tell me who is master.'

But there were some like the wren, the owl and the little brown martin whose nests were hidden in holes. ' How will we know when the hour to sing has come ? ' they asked.

' The red rooster will tell you that,' replied Angus Og, smiling to himself.

Next morning no sooner had the day begun than the red rooster crowed from his perch as Angus Og had promised. First to waken was the lark and he soared upwards, singing his song. He woke the rooks in the trees, the hedge sparrows, thrushes, robins, linnets, until all the birds had joined in the great chorus of song that rang through the forests and far into the mountain glens. Each little bird, even the rook and the jackdaw, made the best of what voice he had.

All through that day Angus Og sat on Ben Cruachan, listening. He clasped his hands, and his laughter was like the wind in the corries, for it was as he had thought. Each bird sang to beat his neighbour, and not one of them could be heard alone.

By sundown the sound of the singing was dying. Even the thrushes and blackbirds were weary and hoarse with their efforts.

' Go to Angus Og on Ben Cruachan,' they told the pigeon, ' and let him tell us who is master.'

But Angus Og shook his head when the pigeon came with his message. ' Indeed it is hard to say. Go back to the birds. Tell them they must sing again tomorrow and every day when the dawn breaks, and I will listen more closely until I have found the master.'

That night, in spite of the long hours of twilight, the birds were glad to rest. But as before the rooster summoned them at daybreak and they tried again. Once more the pigeon went to Angus Og with the message, but Angus Og sent him back with the same reply. Nor did he ever decide who was master, for the singing of the birds made them ready to sleep.

Angus Og still listens to the birds when they sing their dawn chorus. If you doubt the legend, rise in springtime when the rooster crows and you will hear it for yourself. And if you are lucky in the evening, you may even see the wood-pigeon on his way to Ben Cruachan with the question that Angus Og will never answer.

★

Faodar an t-or fhein a cheannach tuille is daor.
Gold itself may be too dearly bought.

THERE was once a shepherd who lived with two faithful
dogs in a small white cottage in the hills beyond Loch
Fyne. One morning he set off to look for sheep that
had strayed across the marches into his neighbours'
territory. His search led him into the glens that lay
between Ben Ime and Ben Vane. High overhead the
larks were singing, and peewits were crying on the
moors. But Col could not find his sheep.

Presently the sun grew so warm he was glad to sit
and rest on the hill-side. His head was soon nodding,
and he might have fallen asleep had not the sudden
chatter of voices come on the wind to rouse him.

He looked about but there was no-one to be seen.
'It must have been the wind in the rushes,' he told
himself as he settled down once again to sleep. But
no sooner was his head on the soft turf than the voices
began to whisper on the wind as before.

This time he turned to see if his dogs had heard the
sound but to his surprise they were gone. '*Ca bheil
sibh? Thigibh an so!* [1] Well this is the strange thing!
What tricks are my ears playing, and where have my
dogs gone?' he wondered as he crossed the hillside.
And then he looked down into a green hollow to see
a little lochan. By its shores a group of people were
gathered about a fire.

Cautiously he went nearer, and very soon was
rubbing the last of the sleep from his eyes. For a score
of fairy creatures clad in garments of the brightest
green, were carrying creels of peat to pile on their fire.
They made such haste and chattered so loudly to each
other that they saw nothing of the watcher on the
hillside.

[1] *Ca bheil sibh? Thigibh an so!* Where are you? Come here!

When the fire was bright they fetched a pot out of the bracken and put it on to boil. A piper then began to play on a reed-pipe, and while the pot boiled and bubbled the fairies danced merrily to the piper's tunes.

The sun climbed higher in the heavens but still the fairies danced, until at last the piper laid aside his pipe and the fun was over. They crowded round the boiling pot and carried it to the edge of the lochan. Out of it they brought a great length of cloth which they washed and laid out to dry.

Col's eyes were wide with wonder, for never before had he seen cloth dyed so vivid and pretty a green. It was brighter than the first blades of corn, more brilliant than the rainbow's hue. Even the first tender fronds of bracken seemed dull by comparison.

' By the Seven Sleepers ! ' whispered Col, ' but is it not the lucky *bodach* I am ! For I have found the place in the mountains where the fairies dye their cloth.'

He lay watching until at last the cloth was dried and gathered up. The fairies lifted the pot from the fire and ran off into the mountain-side. Col sat up suddenly angry with himself. ' Och, och, och, but it is the fool I am ! If I had used my head I could easily have had that pot for myself. And then, *mo thruaighe*,[1] with the magic dye that was in it, it is a rich man I would have been ! '

As he made his way home the more he thought of what he had seen, the more bent he was on going back. But he would go early in the morning. And he would hide himself with the cunning of the little red fox, close to the lochan. Then when the fairies were busy washing their cloth, he would steal the pot.

And so, when the dawn was goose-grey next morning, Col went to the fairy lochan, and settled down to

---

[1] *mo thruaighe*, my grief

wait. At noon the wind suddenly whispered that the wee folk were coming. First he heard their chatter as they hurried through the bracken. Then they came crowding about the shore, some to fetch peats while others kindled the fire with heather roots.

As before, the piper sat down on a hummock and began to play his pipe. The revels began, and it was all that Col could do to resist the merry music. But he knew well enough that if he stirred or even showed the crown of his head, his chance of stealing the *poit dhubh* [1] would be gone.

On they danced in a ring until it seemed to the herd that the piper would never stop. But at last the time came to take the cloth from the dye-pot. With greedy eyes he watched them carry the pot as far as the lochan. Then a strange thing happened.

The wind suddenly changed from west to east. It swept in a chilly blast across the lochan, whirling the smoke from the fairies' fire to where the herd was hidden. He turned his head this way and that, but the smoke stung his eyes and nostrils. Suddenly he sneezed a great sneeze that echoed across the mountain-side.

In an instant the fairies were rushing hither and thither like the little *drilleachan* [2] on a summer shore, crying in their shrill voices, ' *Ruith! ruith! Tha duine tighinn!* ' [3]

The shepherd stumbled to his feet and began to run as fast as he could towards the shore. But he was too late. The fairies saw him, and rushing to guard the secret of the magic pot, they dragged it quickly to the edge of the lochan. By the time Col had reached the place they had emptied the dye into the water and vanished.

---

[1] *poit dhubh*, black pot   [2] *drilleachan*, sandpiper
[3] *Ruith! ruith! Tha duine tighinn!* Run! run! There's a man coming!

'A curse on the black wind!' he gasped, still sneezing, 'but at least I have the cloth of green and the empty pot.' Sure enough the cloth and the boiling pot lay where the fairies had left them. But when the herd went to pick up the cloth it turned into grass that withered to his touch, while the pot broke into little pieces that crumbled into a fine dust.

But something had happened to the little lochan. Its waters were no longer clear, but lay a brilliant green that sparkled in the sunlight, from shore to shore. And to this day Lag Uaine—the green hollow with the fairy lochan above Inveruglas—still holds the colour of the dye spilled from the fairies' dye-pot.

★

Far am bi bo bidh bean, is far am bi bean bidh buarach.

Where there's a cow there will be a woman, and where there's a woman there will be trouble.

32 THE MAGIC MILKING STOOL

NIGHNEAG was beautiful : so small, so neat, so very lovely that by the time she reached sixteen she had the lads from all the neighbouring townships worshipping her. She had dark curls that fell to the nape of her pretty neck, eyes that were large, sparkling and of the deepest blue, and lips that were red as rowanberries.

Of course Nighneag knew that she was beautiful, more beautiful than the neighbours' daughters who watched her pass in envy, for did not Alasdair, Murdo, and och, scores of others tell her so when they met! And of course was there not the little mirror by her window to make it plain for her to see!

Nighneag told herself every day that she was much

too beautiful and fine a lady to spend her life on the edge of a desolate moor, tending a herd of stupid cows, cleaning a croft-house, toiling with her father in the fields. And sorry am I to tell you, but Nighneag was fast becoming a discontented and stupid young woman.

One day as she went to fetch the cows she was so unhappy she spoke her thoughts aloud. She scolded the cattle, telling them bitterly how much work they caused her, when she might be better employed by the mirror tidying her hair, fashioning new gowns to wear and generally making the most of her charms. I may say that the cattle were well used to Nighmeag's sharp tongue and endless complaints. And the fact that they paid not the slightest heed to her made her more exasperated than ever. So that when one day a small voice came out of the heather crying, ' Wait a bit, Nighneag ! Let me catch up with you ! ' she stopped in astonishment. She saw a small woman chasing after her, with a milking stool in her hands.

' Och, och, och, but you go so fast ! ' gasped the stranger. ' I was hearing your words to the cattle beasts. If it is the milking that is troubling you, see now, I have the very thing—a small wee milking stool,' said the little woman, holding up the stool for her to admire.

Nighneag sighed. It was not a small wee milking stool she was after, but someone to do the milking ! Her companion chuckled as she read Nighneag's thoughts. ' Oh, but wait you ! It is no ordinary stool at all. Sit you down by the red cow and see what a difference it makes.'

Nighneag shrugged her shoulders, but she laid the stool by the red cow and began to milk. Whereupon she opened her eyes wide, for there was the pail already brimming with milk, and no effort to it at all !

Next she milked the white cow and then the black. All in two minutes, mark you, and the cows off to graze again as contented as you please. It was a most extraordinary business altogether.

The stranger was laughing heartily. ' Will you be giving me a small wee promise for my stool, Nighneag ? ' she asked.

Nighneag would have given her the shoes from her feet for the wonderful stool, but she simply nodded her head. ' Then,' went on her strange companion, ' promise me you will bear gently with the cattle from this day on. Scold them you may, but hurt them neither with hand nor stick, or the three-legged milking stool will have its revenge.'

Well now, that seemed a simple enough promise to keep. Nighneag nodded her head, thanked the stranger and went off with the wonderful stool. From that day onwards Nighneag found milking a pleasure. But of course there were many other irksome tasks throughout the day, and by and by she began to wish she had something or someone to scrub the floors, clean the pots, thin the turnips and feed the hens. And in no time at all she was back where she started, complaining bitterly from dawn to dusk.

One day as she went to fetch the cows she forgot her promise. Old Beth, the red cow, refused to hurry home. Nighneag picked a stick from the hedge and whacked her haunches soundly. All went well until they reached the byre, then Nighneag sat down to milk on the magic milking stool. The stool's three legs began to bend and clatter merrily. Nighneag began to dance up and down as if she were riding a donkey. Over went the milking pail, and Nighneag found herself being carried outside on the runaway stool. And to her horror when she tried to get off she found she was stuck fast !

They danced round and round the croft, through the nettles, into burns and ditches, by thorn and whin and bramble, until Nighneag was blistered, scratched and torn from head to toe. Her shoes were gone, her gown in ribbons and her hair caught into a hundred knots and tangles. At the edge of the moor the stool leapt high into the air, tossing Nighneag into the heather, and disappeared.

When at last she scrambled to her feet, Murdo the herd, Tom the weaver's son and Alasdair from the neighbouring croft had come to see what was happening. What they saw made them stare. From staring they went on to smile. And then they laughed until they very nearly cried.

Nighneag of course was in tears, and she ran as fast as she could to the pool to bathe her hurts. But when she saw her reflection she began to smile too. Then she laughed, and the strange thing was, the more she laughed the better she felt. The stings and scratches became soothed. The tangles in her hair combed out easily, and indeed she began to feel happier than ever before.

From that day, and in spite of having lost the magic stool, Nighneag was happy and well content with her life. A smile was ever on her lips and she sang happily all day. And she became so beautiful that one day the laird's youngest son chose her for his bride, which you will agree is the right kind of ending to so strange and unusual a story.

*

Tha iomadh doigh air cu a mharbhadh gun a thachadh le im.

There are many ways of killing a dog besides choking him with butter.

33 MACIAIN GHEARR

SOME say that MacIain Ghearr lived in Mull, some at Ardnamurchan. But as he spent much of his time on the high seas it does not matter very much. He was a bold man, with his own kind of courage, and he certainly was resourceful. Often he had to sharpen his wits or surrender to his enemies.

MacIain had been hearing stories of the wealth of a certain island community belonging to Clan *Duine*.[1] There were fat cattle for the lifting, grain in abundance, and money enough to fill the greediest sporrans. But to raid the island he would have to run the gauntlet. The islanders might be taken by surprise, but they

[1] *Duine*, the old name for Campbell

would certainly see to it that MacIain's galley was intercepted on the way home.

MacIain resolved on a bold plan. His black-hulled galley was seen one day sailing southwards. 'I wonder whom MacIain Ghearr is harrying today,' said the islesmen to each other. When they heard he had plundered their neighbours they prepared to attack him. But MacIain's galley never appeared. Only one galley passed, and it was white-hulled.

Yet the reiver's ship it was. The shore side was white as the surf, but the ocean side (which they were not allowed to see) was black as ever! And so MacIain escaped with his booty.

On many occasions MacIain Ghearr played the same trick, his galley painted white on one side, black on the other, and his cunning is remembered in an old proverb :

> ' Tha taobh dubh is taobh ban air,
> Mar a bh'air bata Mhic Iain Ghearr ! '

> (He has a black side and a white side
> Like the boat of the son of John Kerr !)

34 THE WEASEL AND THE FOX

IN the woods near Loch Lomond there lived a fox. Besides his share of poultry (which he stole nightly from the good folks' hen-houses) he had a taste for rabbits. This annoyed his neighbour, a little brown weasel, who was of the opinion that the rabbits were his prey and his alone.

Unfortunately the weasel was no match for the sturdy fox, and often the little animal had to go supperless to bed. For the bold fox had on more than one occasion stolen his supper from under his nose. One day as the weasel was hunting the hedgerows he came upon the gamekeeper fast asleep. By his side lay his gun, his snuff-box and five pairs of fat rabbits.

The weasel knew that the fox was not far off. So, one by one, he carried the rabbits to the edge of the wood. He returned for the snuff-box, then went off to find the fox.

'Come and see what a fine supper I have caught,' he boasted.

'And what could a small bit of a weasel be catching that would interest so fine a hunter as me, myself!' scoffed the fox.

'Indeed, and it is ten fat rabbits I have to show you,' replied the weasel proudly. 'Come and see for yourself.'

The fox went off with the little weasel. Sure enough there were the rabbits laid out in a row. 'Indeed you have done well this day,' agreed the fox in evident surprise. 'But tell me, how did you manage it, small one?'

'Och, it was simple enough,' said the weasel. 'I made myself as strong as a man. I sniffed the keeper's magic powder, and in no time at all I had the strength of ten such as you. I found that I could outrun the fastest rabbit. But of course I was not trying very hard to begin with. I contented myself with ten rabbits for a start, and there they are for you to see.'

The fox was very interested, especially in the magic powder that the weasel had mentioned. 'Would you care to try it for yourself, my friend?' invited the weasel.

The fox looked at the snuff-box. 'Indeed, and I would,' he replied. If the weasel could catch ten rabbits then he could catch ten times that number.

'Look then,' said the wily weasel, 'open the lid and sniff a very small sniff. And I wager there will not be your equal for strength nor swiftness.'

The fox snatched the snuff-box greedily, opened the lid, and emptied it in one great sniff. Almost at once it seemed his nose had gone on fire! He began to howl in anguish, and his sneezing echoed the length and breadth of the wood.

Meanwhile the weasel had slipped off to where the keeper lay sleeping. He nipped his ear to wake him up, then hid in the long grass. The man rose angrily. He looked around to see what had disturbed him. Then he heard the din from the wood near by. Clutching his gun he hurried to see what was the matter, leaving the weasel chuckling in the grass.

The little animal listened eagerly. Presently there was a loud bang, and the sneezing and howling ceased in an instant.

That night as the weasel went home he saw the fox's brush hanging by a nail outside the keeper's cottage. It told him that from then on he could catch and eat his supper without a thieving fox stealing it from him. And the gamekeeper was just as pleased, for he had rid the countryside of at least one poultry thief.

GLAG AG GLAODHAICH
(*Ding dong bell*)

An glag ag glaodhaich cobhair
'S a' phiseach anns an tobar.
Co a chuir ann i ?
Co chuir ach Anndra !
Co a thug as i ?
Co thug ach Peadar !
Nach b'e sin am peasan crosd'
A dhol a bhathadh piseag bhochd
Nach do rinn de chron air thalamh
Ach sealg nan luch an sabhal athar !

*

Is minig a bha 'n donas daicheil.

The Devil is often attractive.

35   THE EACH UISGE [1]

ANNA, the little herdmaid, was resting, but she kept an eye on the cattle, especially Peggac the little brown heifer. For whenever the chance came the wayward animal would wander off, taking the herd with her.

So when Peggac suddenly lowed, Anna watched closely. She saw first Peggac then the others rise to stare as a dark shape approached from the lochans. The little girl saw that it was a horse with a long mane and tail, and a coat that was blacker than the *boobrie's* [2] wings. This was puzzling, for she knew of no-one who had such an animal in the neighbourhood.

Next day the horse appeared again, and every day for a week, each day coming closer to the cattle until

[1] *each uisge*, ' water-horse,' a demon living in mountain tarns which feeds on flesh
[2] *boobrie*, a mythical bird that spreads its wings across the sky at dusk

they paid little heed to its presence. Only Peggac seemed uneasy.

Anna told her parents of the strange horse on the moor. They too were uneasy for they knew that an *each uisge* lived in the lochan where the lilies grew. 'You must run home when it appears, Anna,' said her father. 'It is an evil creature out of the lochan. Many a man has been drowned by the *each uisge*.'

'But it was a great fine creature, father,' persisted the little girl. 'Could we not tame it to fetch our peats from the moor on its broad back?'

'There is but one way to catch and tame such a beast. Seize the halter it wears and it is powerless. And lucky is the man who has such a horse, for it will work without stopping with the strength of ten. Indeed, I would be the proud man if I had the courage to face such a beast!'

Anna saw the *each uisge* every day. By then Peggac the heifer had lost her fear of it. But the *each uisge* was only waiting its chance. One day without warning it sprang towards the little herd, striking down Peggac. Its teeth sank in the heifer's neck and it began to drag her towards the lochan.

The little girl ran for her father, who returned with the dogs and drove it off. But the heifer was dead. He decided that he must find a way to destroy the beast lest Anna herself be taken. He skinned the hide from the dead cow, dried it in the sun, then stitched it up and stuffed it with bracken. Next day he put on the hide himself and lay in the heather as Peggac might have done.

Presently the *each uisge* appeared. It saw the cow that rested on the moor and made its slow approach. The weeds and slime clung to its coat, and a thick halter swung from its neck. When its fiery breath was on him Anna's father grasped the rope and held tight. The creature reared and plunged in a fury to escape. But the man held fast. Leaping up he was soon astride the animal and at once it became quiet.

For many years the black horse lived on the little croft. It was easily managed and worked tirelessly all day. Not once did it attempt to return to the waters of the lochan. And then one day Anna found a halter in a corner of the loft. She decided that such a fine halter would fit the black horse, forgetting that this was the very halter the creature had brought with it from the moor many years ago.

She slipped the rope over its mane and leapt upon its back as she had done a hundred times. For a moment the horse stood still, then with a wild cry it wheeled suddenly and bolted across the moor towards the lily lochan.

The crofter of Duirinish paid dearly for his folly, for Anna was never seen again.

*

Cha mhisde sgeul mhath aithris da uair.
A good tale is none the worse for being twice told.

36 THE WITCHES OF MULL

As everyone knows, the survivors of the great Armada from Spain had cause to rue the day they sighted the Scottish coast. Here is a tale from the isle of Mull which concerns witchcraft and how it was used to destroy one of the enemy's ships.

The dwellers on the island were one day stirred to see several fine ships fleeing before a gathering storm. Before the day was out the storm was sweeping the coastline. Angry clouds hid the retreating Armada, and even angrier seas were making it hard for them to find shelter. The night wore on, without any lull in the fury of wind and wave, and it was clear that more than one galleon would never return to Spain.

Dawn came, and with the lifting of the shadows and a slackening tide the wind fell. Watchers searched the strands for signs of shipwreck. All at once a cry went up. A child had found the body of a beautiful maiden cast high upon the rocks of a little cove.

That day the Spanish lady, no less than the daughter of the King of Spain, was buried in a rude grave by the seashore, unattended by priest or mourner, and unmarked even by a wooden cross. Eventually news of her death reached Spain, and the king swore vengeance on a people who had shown so little feeling for a princess as to deny her Christian burial. He turned to an adventurer by the name of Captain Forrest, who professed, among other accomplishments, to have skill in the black arts as well as direct dealings with the Prince of Darkness himself.

When it became known on the island that the ruthless captain planned to pillage every village and dwelling, and destroy by fire and sword every man, woman and child, the islanders gathered to decide what preparations they would make to meet the invader.

The Lord Duart it was who begged that they might match witchcraft with witchcraft. ' Let word be taken to each and every warlock and witch-wife between Mishnish and Erraid, Treshnish and Loch Don ! ' he declared. ' Let them have word that a wizard seeks to take and hold the island of Mull for himself.'

From near and far came the Doideagan Muileach, the grey witches. Some rode on oat-straws, some flew as daws or carrion crows and many came hidden in the cloak of the wind, until the earth trembled to their fearful clamour. When they were assembled Duart addressed the Doideagan Mor, a haggard beldam whose one eye saw only in the night. He pleaded that a mighty storm be conjured up to sink the approaching ship.

' Magic to break magic ! ' screeched the hag. ' But no magic may destroy that which comes from the hand of God. Has the wizard sought help from the Deity ? '

In reply Duart assured the witch that Forrest was an unbeliever. This satisfied the witches and they planned the form the counter-spell would take. Green bracken was brought and twined and fashioned into a rope. At one end a grindstone was fastened, then the loose end was slung over a gibbet-tree. The Doideagan Mor began to pull. The rope tightened, and the stone began to rise from the ground. Almost at once the wind rose, increasing as the stone lifted inch by inch.

But the witch had no more strength to master Forrest's spell. The wind blew no harder and she screamed for her sisters to help. But their efforts were in vain. The weight still hung heavily. Even the muscles of the great smith and his hammer-man were useless.

At last they called for Gormal, the greatest and

ugliest of all witches, to come and lay her hand upon
the bracken rope. She came on the lightning, a
hideous creature with a countenance that hurt men's
eyes, and seized the rope. The great stone flew
upwards to the summit of Ben More, where it remains
to this day, and a storm broke that rocked the earth
beneath their feet.

Meantime Captain Forrest's brig could be seen,
driven before the mountainous seas, plunging towards
the guardian rocks. And as the thunder rolled and
lightning seared a sky black as the deepest pit, the
ship struck. The Captain and his crew of Spaniards
perished, to find a last resting-place on the shores
they sought to plunder.

The witches departed in a whirlwind, but the echoes
of their victory may still be heard in song and story
in odd forgotten corners of the Western Isles.

*

Am fear a tha na thamh, tha e na leth-trom an fhearain.
He who is idle is a burden on the land.

37 FAIRY GOLD

SEUMAS MACVEAN was the biggest and the laziest man
in Ross-shire. He was also a grand piper. And as
he had the good nature that very often accompanies
a liking for taking things easy, he was liked by
everyone.

Unfortunately it was his wife Mari who had to bear
the brunt of his shortcomings. She was as small and
energetic as her husband was large and slow-moving.
But there were times when she was almost at her
wits' end to know where to begin, for as well as the
housework she had the water to draw, the peats to

carry, the cows to look to and the hens to feed. And then there was the neglected croft to be looked after.

It was the state of the fields that worried her most of all. Fortunately there were only two of them that could be seen from the road, but they were no credit to the big crofter. While Seumas was off somewhere playing his pipes or fishing for trout, the cattle would be knocking down the dykes, the sheep straying or catching themselves in the brambles, and the rushes and bracken marching in strength across the neglected acres.

Winter passed and the time came for the crofters to plant their potatoes. Round about, the little families could be seen ploughing and sowing while the good weather lasted. But Seumas's seed-potatoes were still where they had lain in their boxes, with sprouts on them twice the length of the biggest earthworm. Mari stormed and raged, but all that Seumas did was smile his friendliest smile, assuring her that once he had rested his strength he would undertake the job. Then he would stroll off with his chanter or his fishing-rod for the rest of the day.

This state of affairs went on until Mari could stand it no longer. One day she sat down in the kitchen and wept. She became so depressed she pulled off the wedding-ring from her finger and was on the point of throwing it out of the window, when an idea suddenly struck her.

She went to her trinket box and emptied it on her lap. She picked out three brass farthings and a soldier's button and wrapped them up with her ring in the corner of a handkerchief. Then she took the spade and a box of seed-potatoes and went out into the field.

With a large round stone she hammered the coins and the brass button until they all looked almost alike, rubbed and polished them till they shone like dull gold, then began to dig. Every now and then she buried one under the soil, and when the last of them had been hidden she returned to the cottage.

When Seumas returned that evening, Mari closed the door carefully behind him and put up the bar. 'Seumas,' she whispered, 'I have made a strange discovery. Today I went to plant the potatoes in the field. I had scarcely turned a spit when I found a ring hidden in the earth. It was not much to look at until I polished it hard, but I am thinking that it is made of gold!' Mari untied the corner of the handkerchief and showed him the shining ring.

Seumas stared and stared as the gold shone in the sunset, not for one moment thinking that it was his own wife's wedding-ring.

'Aye indeed,' he whispered in reply, taking it in his hand. 'It is a fine ring and real gold without a doubt. That was lucky, Mari. And in the potato field, you say?'

'Yes, Seumas. And if I had not been so tired I might have dug a little longer, for I am thinking there may be more where that came from. Would it not be the grand thing if we had found the place where the fairies hide their treasure!'

Seumas's eyes were bright, for he had been thinking that very same thought. 'Fairy gold! I have heard such tales before! Och now, if that was the case, not another stroke of work would I need to be doing for evermore! But I have dug that field over and over again, and I have never seen anything there but rocks and stones.'

'That was because you never dug deep enough, Seumas. Oh, if I were a strong man like yourself, I tell you I would not be sparing the spade or myself when so much might be hidden under the sods!'

Now Seumas was lazy, but this was something that appealed greatly to his imagination. Already he was seeing himself filling bag after bag with treasure that his spade uncovered. Next morning, therefore, he awoke long before dawn, and was for marching off on the treasure hunt without even a bite of breakfast, when his wife peeped over the bedclothes.

' I have been thinking, Seumas,' she said, ' that it would be better and more natural if you were to plant the potatoes as you dig. For if the neighbours thought for one moment that it was treasure you were seeking they would be round about you and watching all the time.'

Seumas agreed that it was good advice, and he carried the seed-potatoes with him to the field. When the neighbours awoke they were astonished to see Seumas MacVean hard at it, digging and planting potatoes, as if his life depended upon it. And I can tell you the rooks and the gulls had a grand feast of worms, for Seumas drove the spade three spits deep and broke the soil into the smallest pieces.

But after he had been digging for more than two hours his first fine enthusiasms were beginning to leave him. His back was beginning to ache from the unusual exercise, and he might even have thrown down the spade in disgust if there hadn't been a clink of metal against metal. Seumas's eyes suddenly goggled for he had uncovered the soldier's button! He picked it up excitedly and tried to understand what it was. It completely mystified him, but he was quite sure from its colour that it was gold.

The find was enough to raise his drooping spirits. He went on digging and planting with renewed hope. A few minutes later he found one of the farthings, and he almost danced a reel for joy. Seumas was now convinced he was on the verge of a great discovery.

He toiled on for the rest of the day, stopping only once to swallow food. Whenever he felt tired the jingle in his pocket urged him to greater efforts. The neighbours watching from their crofts were quite sure that Seumas's mind had gone ; for nothing that they could think of could have made him change overnight from a happy-go-lucky idler to a man of such determination and industry.

At last the field was dug from end to end and seed-potatoes snugly planted in every drill. Seumas by then was almost dropping with exhaustion and disappointment. He had found no more treasure than Mari had hidden. That night he crawled into bed with the ring, the three farthings and the soldier's button under his pillow, and fell into a sleep that lasted a night and a day.

Mari was delighted that her plan had worked so well, but she was sorry when she looked at her weary husband asleep in bed. Never had she known him to sleep so profoundly or snore so loudly before ! When he awoke he stretched his aching body, remembering his vain search for gold, and immediately put his hand under the pillow to make sure he hadn't been dreaming. There was nothing there ! Mari had returned the ring to her finger, and dropped the rest of the little collection into the well.

' I might have said I was dreaming, but from the pains and aches in my shoulders and my back I remember digging in the field. I found some coins, as well as the ring that you found. Where are they now, tell me ? '

' The fairies must have come to take back what was their own while you slept, Seumas. And they will have hidden them somewhere on the croft. Maybe if you were to dig again . . .'

Seumas groaned aloud at the very idea, and fell

asleep again. Next morning he dressed himself, ate a hearty breakfast and went off to fish for trout. Mari sighed as she watched him slip back into his old ways, but she smiled to herself, for at least the potatoes were planted !

38 THE GREY GOOSE

THE owl on silent wings, with its mysterious voice crying in the dusk, was ever a bird of ill omen. Like the raven, the grey crow and others of their kind, it was supposed to presage disaster and doom. On the other hand the robin and its companion Jenny Wren were welcomed by everyone and held dear in song and story. But the swan and the wild goose, night-flying against the moon, trumpeting their stirring music out of the dark heavens, roused the imagination in a different way, and gave rise to many legends of romance and high adventure.

One day, so the *cailleachs* tell, a king fell foul of a grisly beldame, a witch within whose bubbling cauldron lay the vilest spells. This foul creature took

116

her revenge by waylaying the king's daughter as she walked by the shores of Loch Sunart. She ringed the maiden within a magic circle, transforming her into a grey goose [1] that spread its wings and flew northwards to the land of ice and snow.

No-one knew what had befallen the maiden save the witch. She was sought far and wide for many months, but in the end the search was abandoned. It was believed that she had been devoured by the wolves, or spirited away by the fairy folk. But the princess had a lover, a fair prince, and he continued to seek her in the mountains and the forests. For a year he roamed far and wide, living on the birds of the air, the animals of the woodlands and the fish in the river. He was a mighty hunter whose skill with the bow was uncanny, and it was not hard for him to strike down the hindmost goose in the gaggle that flew one evening across the saltings.

It fell mortally wounded not far from him, and he strode quickly to gather his prize. He reached the bird as the breath left its body. At that instant its form changed, and the young man was horrified to find himself bending over the still form of his beloved princess. In despair he plucked the arrow from her heart, breaking it in three pieces, grinding them underfoot. Tenderly he laid his plaid over her and knelt to mourn his beloved.

Meantime the geese flew in wide circles calling their stricken companion to join them. But the prince heard nothing for he had died as he knelt in sorrow over his princess. The life that had passed from him entered the body of the princess. She stirred as if rising from a deep sleep, once again assuming the form of a goose that spread its pinions in answer to the summons of its kind.

[1] *grey goose*, greylag goose

From the broken arrow grew the first trees of the mighty forest of Caledon. The plaid that had lain over the princess became a broad green sward still to be seen on upper Speyside. And when the stars crackle with winter frost, the voice of a lonely grey goose can still be heard calling down the valleys of the high Grampians.

MEILEAG! A CHAORA DHUBH
(Baa, baa, black sheep)

> Meileag! A chaora dhubh,
> Bheil cloimh agad an drasd'?
> Tha, dhuin'-uasail, sin agam.
> Tri poca lan—
> Aon do'n mhaishistir,
> Aon do bhean-an-taighe,
> Is aon do'n a ghille bheag
> Tha fuireach san t-sraid chuil.

39 A LEGEND OF MACFIE

THIS tale is heard in so many forms that it would be rash to say that what follows is nearest of them all to the truth.

Macfie of Colonsay was a strong man and a mighty hunter. He had seven sons, all of them tall and comely. As befitted islesmen they were skilled in the sailing of boats, and often the chief's galley could be seen on its way to Jura or some neighbouring island where the hunting was good.

One day Macfie himself was returning from the moors of Colonsay. Darkness had fallen early, and mist had come in from the sea, so that Macfie was hard put to it to find his way. When it seemed that he would have to seek some corner to shelter until the dawn came, he stumbled upon a small grey house set against the hillside. Macfie knew every inch of the island but he had no recollection of having seen this *bochan* [2] before. But darkness and mist change the form and colour of familiar things and he laid the fault on his bad memory. He peered in the window to see an old woman stirring porridge by the fire.

He was a hungry man, and he presented himself to the crone and begged a bite of food and a bed for the night. He was made welcome (indeed it seemed that his visit had been awaited), and a bowl of porridge was set for him. While he supped, his eye fell on a great hound that lay with two pups in a dark corner.

'My mind is failing me, for surely I have never seen that hound before,' he remarked.

'That may be,' replied the old woman, 'for the hound is lame and cannot travel far. But once she hunted with the strength of the lion and the eye of the eagle.' The old woman then went on to relate ancient tales of how the great hound had outstripped all others in courage and cunning at the chase. Macfie's interest was kindled at once.

'So valiant a mother must surely have borne whelps to match her in speed and courage,' he said, looking closely at the sleeping pups.

'Of that I have little doubt,' was the reply. 'Yourself has the hunter's eye, Macfie. Which pup would you choose?'

Macfie looked again, and saw that they were of equal size, but one was brindled like the mother, the other blacker than the raven's wing. 'For my part I would choose the black,' he decided at length.

'Then it will travel with you on the morrow,' said the old woman. 'Treat it well, Macfie. Be patient

[2] *bochan*, small cottage

and forbearing with it always and the day will come when it will repay you with its life.'

Next day Macfie carried home with him the black pup. The woman would take no payment, but she repeated her wish that the animal be well cared for, and once more assured him that it would repay his kindness with its life. But though he tried repeatedly to return to the *bochan* hidden in the hills his searching was in vain. Nor was any woman answering to his description known throughout the island.

In time the black pup grew up and promised well, for it learned quickly, showed more than usual intelligence and possessed great strength and fleetness of foot. At last the day came when Macfie decided it was ready for the hunt.

' Tomorrow we will go to Jura,' he told his seven sons, ' and we will match the black hound with the red stags of that island.' The boat was made ready against the voyage, but when the time came for them to depart, the black hound stood stubbornly on the shore and would not enter the boat. When they tried to force it aboard the galley it turned tail and ran to the hills. Macfie was disappointed, but he restrained his sons from hunting it down and chastising it. ' We will try the hound another day. It may be that it is afraid of the sea.'

But though Macfie went many times with his sons to Jura, not once would the hound accompany them even to the shore.

' The hound is useless, fit meat for the hoody crows,' scoffed the young men, who by this time would have slain it without hesitation.

But as before Macfie stayed them. ' His day will surely come,' he told them, remembering the words of the mysterious old woman.

One day they prepared to return for the last time

that season to Jura. 'What of the black hound!' joked the young men. 'Where will it hide itself today?' Macfie made no reply, for as usual the hound had taken himself elsewhere. But on their way to launch the galley, great was their astonishment. The black hound leapt before them across the sand and sprang aboard the galley without bidding.

Thereafter the voyage was made beneath a cloudless sky, and the galley sped before a steady wind. The black hound was first to reach the shores of Jura, and could scarcely be curbed as the hunters climbed towards the deer forests. Then, at the first corrie in the hills, it halted and refused to lead or follow. As before it resisted capture, and Macfie was forced to leave the sullen creature to skulk amongst the crags.

But before the party reached the first summit a change of weather threatened. Black clouds rolled up from the west, and a gale struck the island. The darkness fell so suddenly that Macfie and his sons made haste to return to the boat. But the fury of wind and rain drove them to shelter in a cave, and there they waited while thunder rolled from hill to hill, and the fierce gale plucked the heather from the slopes and tossed it into the darkness.

At last sleep came to the hunters one by one, until Macfie alone was left to listen to the howling of the wind, his eyes ever on the mouth of the cave. It seemed to him that he saw a shadow enter, and he felt a warm heavy body lay itself at his feet. The black hound had returned. The storm increased in fury. Macfie shivered in the darkness for now it seemed that the powers of evil had followed the black hound, and were gathering about him in the cave. The hound too was restless, stirring every now and then and growling in its throat.

Suddenly a hand touched Macfie and closed about

his neck. He started up but was at once flung against the wall of the cavern. At that moment the black hound sprang to the attack and grappled with the unseen enemy. Macfie cowered while the conflict continued, deafened by the howls of anguish and fury that echoed from wall to wall, calling for his sons to rise. At length the combatants were locked across his body; the breath was driven from him and he fell back unconscious. No more did he know until he awoke in the grey light of daybreak.

He looked about him. His seven sons lay as if in sleep, but each of them was dead. Across his feet was spread the broken body of the black hound, its teeth holding a bloodstained hand and arm wrenched from some gigantic body. At that his reason left him and he fled the cave.

Macfie returned to Colonsay with his story that is talked of yet. Within a month he had grown an old and feeble man, but he would not rest until he returned with retainers to the cave on Jura. The bodies of his seven sons had vanished, as had the great hand and arm. And when it seemed that the tale he had told was no more than his imaginings, the islanders saw in a cleft of rock the body of the black hound. And the horror of its shape and the scars of burning everywhere convinced them that it had fought with something beyond the ken of mortal man.

*

Cha robh math na olc riamh gun mhnathan uime.
There never was good or ill without women being concerned in it.

AODH, son of Aodh, fisherman of Isle Oronsay, was out
in the bay in his own small coracle, drifting in the
slack water. Sometimes he fished for the flat-fish
lurking in the sand in the shallow water, and sometimes he lay in the stern doing nothing at all.

The summer heat had gone from the sun, for the
season was nearly spent. Already the hand of autumn
was laid upon the land, bleaching the sea-grass and
spreading gold and russet and earth-brown across the
moor and the gentle uplands. Aodh loved the bay of
golden sand where the little ducks came in winter, but
better still he loved the little outer isles and their
narrow creeks where the shoals of white fish gathered.

Yard by yard the coracle drifted towards the sand-
bars, out into the blue open water where the seals
played. Aodh decided he would put about before
meeting the full blast of the wind. But when he plied
the oars he knew he had been foolish. A sudden squall
swung the vessel into the current. It began to drift
seawards on a course of its own.

No-one saw Aodh leave the bay, to vanish round
the last headland. By nightfall the hills of home had
gone, the night clouds had lowered, and the frail
coracle tossed helplessly before the rising wind. When
it seemed that the waves must bring about disaster,
a flock of oyster-catchers flew out of the darkness to
circle the coracle. Where they flew the sea became
calm and the wind had no power upon the waves.

The birds remained until the dawn broke. A green
isle appeared upon the horizon, and to it the birds
flew swiftly, leaving Aodh to bring the coracle into
calm water, without shoal or ripple. He dragged it
high up a smooth strand. But the sudden uncanny
stillness roused in him a little fear that he had sailed

beyond the world, and made him plunge his knife into a hillock as he had been told to do. For the wise fishermen said that to do this would drive away the powers of evil.

Suddenly he heard someone singing in a sweet voice. He followed the sound and saw a maiden seated on a rock. Tall she was, and slender as the birch-tree. Her golden hair fell on white shoulders, and her face was lovelier than that of any maiden he had ever known. She called him to her side, and as he sat at her feet he knew he would love her for ever.

The years passed. Each day that dawned upon the green isle increased his love for the maiden. Never had he known such happiness. The sun had never shone so brightly. It was indeed a place of ever-lasting peace, without shadow of unhappiness. But the day came when Aodh began to dream of Isle Oronsay. He tried to put the thoughts from him, but each day they returned more urgently, in the end leading him back to the shore where his coracle lay above the gentle tide.

At length he decided to sail again to the land he had almost forgotten. When he told the maiden of his longing she grew sad.

' That cannot be, Aodh, son of Aodh. Seven years you have lived on Tir-nan-og—the Land of the Ever Young—from which there is no return.'

' My coracle is sound, and still will float,' he replied.

' No farther than a span from the shore, beloved. Then return it must—or sink beneath the bed of the sea.'

Then Aodh realised that for all its beauty this isle of everlasting youth was no more than a prison holding them both captive. But he did not tell her of the dagger thrust in the little hill by the shore that would still let him go free.

In the morning she followed him to the beach. 'Come with me as far as the point yonder,' he said as he set the coracle in the water.

'There and no farther can either of us go,' she replied as she stepped into the craft.

But when he reached the point of land he turned the bow seawards, riding the waves steadily into the east.

But no sooner had they reached the open sea than a change came upon the maiden. Aodh found her weeping in the stern, and with each tear that fell it seemed a little of her beauty faded.

For three days and three nights they sailed on a troubled sea. Then with the fourth dawn the outline of Isle Oronsay appeared on the horizon. Aodh steered the coracle into the safety of the bay he knew so well.

Aodh leapt ashore and turned towards the maiden. 'Come now, best-beloved,' he cried happily. 'Come with me to my own house upon the hill, where no evil spell can befall us.'

The maiden made no reply. He called her again. She cowered against the rocks, with her head turned to where the gulls were wheeling and the oyster-catchers piped on the far rocks, her shawl gathered close about her. He called her a third time, approaching to pull aside the shawl as he lifted her lightly in his arms. When at last she turned he no longer saw the form and face of a young and beautiful maiden, but the shrivelled features and crooked body of an ancient crone.

'O Aodh, son of Aodh!' she wept in sorrow, 'let us return to the green isle where I may find my youth again and keep it for ever!'

With a heavy heart Aodh realised that the old tales were true. Those who returned from the enchanted isle forfeited not only youth and beauty but happiness. He took his loved one by the hand, turned his back

125

on Isle Oronsay for ever, and together they put to sea to seek the Land of Lost Content.

Sometimes the fishermen of the isles tell a tale of how a lonely coracle appears upon the horizon, on its endless search for Tir-nan-og, the Land of the Ever Young. But always the wind comes and it vanishes as mysteriously as it appears. When it happens they look to their sheets, for they have come to know that surely a storm is on its way.

SEINN PORT NAN SIA SGILLINN
(*Sing a song of sixpence*)

Seinn port nan sgillinn,
Mo phocaid lan siol dubh ;
Ann am broinn a 'bhonnaich mhoir
Tha corr is fichaed druid.

Nuair chaidh am bonnaich fhosgladh suas
'S ann sheinn na h-eoin le spid ;
Nach b'e sin an truinnsear breagh'
G'a chur air beulaobh righ.

Bha 'n righ an taigh an ionmhais
Ag cunntadh suas gach sgillinn ;
Bha bhan-righ anns a' chulaist
'S i 'g itheadh mir is mil air.

Bha 'n t-searbhant anns a' gharadh
Cur aodach air an rop ;
Nuas druid dhubh le sian
Is spion e dhith an t-sron.

*

Eallach mor an duine leisg.
The lazy man finds all burdens heavy.

41 THE FAIRY COBBLER

EWAN GRANT worked harder than most crofters on the lands of Alligin on Loch Torridon. Indeed and he had to, for the ground he tilled was sour where it was not stony, the ditches were seldom dry since the rain fell heaviest and the snow lay longest on his side of the mountains. No matter how hard he worked two weeds sprang up where one had been before, and Ewan was hard put to it to make a living.

And so Ewan, the quiet hard-working crofter, remained poor until the day he cast himself on a green hillock to rest his bones and bemoan his lot. Oh, these hillocks and humplocks in the Highland places! Few there must have been that the wee folks had not bewitched or put a ring round with their dancing feet. Ewan's couch was green and comfortable, the wind was as soft as the mouse's ear, and the sun warm as the thrush's breast. But there was no rest for him, for there came a tap-tap-tapping to keep his eyes from closing.

At first he thought it was the stone-chat striking his pebbles behind the whins. But no birds were there on the peaceful hillside. Ewan listened closely. The sound came from under his very ear! He peeped into a little hole no bigger than a rabbit's scrape to see a wee small brownie at work at a last mending shoes. As he watched the *Brogaire Beg* [1] yawned. ' Old bones—slow bones! Tired it is I am! Day in, day out and here I sit mending, patching, stitching and nailing shoes for others to wear! Now if I were spry enough to reach the top of Ben Alligin yonder and dip into the treasure crock would I not be the rich and happy *brogaire*! Aye indeed, but my back

[1] *Brogaire Beg*, Little Cobbler

is crooked as the fox's leg and my legs shorter than
the mole's. Hard enough is it for me to climb into
my own bed at night without thinking of reaching to
the top of the world!'

Ewan, who was himself feeling much the same as
the brownie, listened to every word. He put his
mouth to the hole and whispered, 'Good day to you,
Brogaire Beg, and you might have been speaking for
myself. Weary I am with hard work, but my legs
will still carry me. If as you say there is treasure at
the top of Ben Alligin then maybe I could be finding
it for you!'

'Say that again, red-headed man!' cried the
brownie, looking up at Ewan, who repeated his words.
'The very thing!' chuckled the wee man. 'Now
listen! At the top of the mountain there is a grey

128

stone and a black one, side by side. And in between
there is a white chuckie-stone as big as your head and
seven times as heavy. Put your hand to the chuckie-
stone and roll it over. Underneath there lies a crock
filled to the rim with gold pieces.'

'If there is,' replied Ewan, 'then I'll put it on my
shoulders and bring it here before the sun sets and we
will share the treasure between us.'

'You will not!' cried the brownie, tapping Ewan
with a stumpy finger. 'You will take from the pot
no more than will fill your sporran. And for every
piece of gold you take I'll take three!'

Ewan was pleased to agree and leave it at that. So
off he went, all weariness forgotten, to the mountain-
top, where after much searching he found the grey
stone and the black with a great white chuckie in
between. He rolled the white stone aside and saw a
crock buried in the peat that was filled to the brim
with glittering golden coins. It was hard to resist
filling not only his sporran but his black bonnet as
well with the treasure, but he obeyed the brownie's
words and set off down the mountain to Loch Torridon.

The brownie was there to greet him when he returned.
And they sat side by side in the sunset counting the
gold. For every piece that went to Ewan, three fell
in the brownie's lap. But to Ewan's surprise when
the gold was divided, by some magic both lots were
exactly alike.

'Thanks to me for telling you!' cried the manikin.
'And hi-ri-ho-ro!—thanks to your long legs, we have
gold to take home with us!' And with a skip and a
caper the fairy cobbler disappeared into the hillock.

Well, Ewan bought a herd of cows, a score of sheep,
hens to lay, a pig to fatten, two chairs, a table, fine
linen to cover a new soft bed, and much that I have
forgotten. And it was not long before news of sudden

wealth was spread abroad. ' Tell me where it came from ? ' wheedled Finlay his neighbour one day. And foolishly Ewan told him of the *Brogaire Beg* and the crock of gold at the top of Ben Alligin. Now there were greedy men on Loch Torridon, but the greediest was Finlay. Off he went to climb the mountain. On reaching the summit he made haste to find the treasure, rolling each boulder aside until in the end he found the white chuckie that covered the crock.

' Aha ! ' he cried as he let the gleaming gold pieces spill through his fingers. ' Ewan Grant is the rich man, but there is gold enough here to make me ten—even twenty times as rich ! ' He filled his sporran, his bonnet, his hose taken from his feet, and his brogues. He made a sack of his tattered shirt and filled it too. Sad he was he could not fill his mouth and his two fists with what little was left. But it could be hidden against his return on the morrow.

With the great weight of gold bending him double he struggled back to Torridon. As he passed the cobbler's hillock he jumped when a squeaky voice cried out, ' You will keep one piece and I'll take three ! ' Finlay looked down to see the brownie peeping out of his hole in the earth.

' Not a groat shall I give you ! ' growled the mean man. He was so furious at being seen with his burden, that he thrust out his bare foot to crush the life out of the little cobbler. But the brownie was as quick as a weasel, and Finlay's foot struck another hole in the earth. At once the earth fell inwards and Finlay found himself slipping into a giant pit that grew and grew.

With a great fear on him he flung aside first one bundle of gold, then another, until he lay clutching the earth, with only the sporran full of gold left. But the pit opened wider so that to save himself he released his hold on the precious sporran. Immediately he was able to find his way back to the top of the pit where he lay exhausted.

When he opened his eyes again he was astonished to find the hillock exactly as it had been—green and smooth, and with no more than a small scrape that a rabbit might have made at his feet. He ran home as if all the fiends of the darkness were at his heels, and kept the tale of his adventure to himself.

However from that day it was to be noticed that Finlay the crofter became kindly, helpful and generous to his neighbours, and he lived long enough to enjoy a fair measure of prosperity which was perhaps more than he deserved.

42 THE SEAL-MAIDEN

IN the Hebrides and particularly in the islands of Orkney and Shetland, many strange tales are told about the seals. These shy sea-creatures were held in awe by the islanders many years ago. At one time no man could be persuaded to kill a seal, for they were believed to be drowned mariners come back to earth again in the guise of beasts. And certainly for those who have heard the mournful half-human voices of the creatures as they gather to rest on some lonely reef, or plunge and frolic beneath the waves, it is not hard to believe the ancient superstitions.

One tale tells of a young fisherman who lived on Pomona, the old name for the mainland of Orkney. He had gone with several companions to the fishing grounds off the Holm of Boray. It was midsummer, the time of year when the sun's setting makes little difference to the light left in the northern sky. The little fleet made ready and set off in good spirits, for the wind was favourable and gave promise of fine weather.

Before they had gone very far, however, the wind changed. The sky became overcast, and just before sundown a great bank of grey fog rolled in from the sea. The fishermen tried hard to hold to their course and keep together. But one by one they vanished into the gloom of the fog.

The young man drifted alone and in growing fear, for the coasts were treacherous with hidden rocks and endless skerries. Presently the fog grew thinner and he was able to see, a little way off, the outline of a promontory. As he drew nearer he found it bleak and inhospitable. But he was glad to put ashore without further mishap, and he wondered if his companions had shared his good fortune.

After securing his boat against the making tide, he set off to discover where he was and if there was a house near by to give him shelter. He had not gone far before he heard voices and music. It filled him with relief, and he believed he was about to join his companions. Just then he began to notice the skins of seals still wet from the sea laid out on every rock. It was a strange discovery, but the sight he saw when he climbed the highest rock was even stranger.

Instead of a group of fishermen gathered about their boats, he saw a great company of strangers feasting and dancing on the shore. Only then did he remember it was the Eve of St John, the night of festival of the sea-folk, when all the selkies [1] swim ashore to cast their skins, and, in the form once more of men and women, to spend the twilight hours in merrymaking.

The young fisherman hid himself to watch the revelry, and listen to the music that shrieked and

---

[1] *selkie*, a seal

132

sobbed like the wind on the sea. One by one the stars came out. The mist gathered about the dancers, then vanished on the breeze. And then, when the dance was at its height, the slow sound of the bell of Saint Magnus' Church came faintly across the sea.

It struck the hour of midnight, the time when the seal-folk must cease their merriment, find their skins and return to the sea for another year.

Beside the fisherman lay a little tawny skin and a garland of brightly coloured seaweed. He could see the figures on the beach transform themselves from humans into seals as they found their skins. Soon the owner of the tawny skin would come. He wondered what form the creature would take.

He had scarcely time to creep behind the rocks, clutching the skin in his hand, when a maiden crossed the sand. Her hair was tawny as the skin, and her beauty and grace reminded him of the little kitti-wakes on the ledges of the limy sea caves. She wound the garland about her hair then began to search for her skin.

When at length she realised that it had gone, and that she could not follow the great company of seals out to sea, she wept. And it was the same sad sound that a seal makes when it comes ashore to suckle its calf. It made the fisherman sad to hear it, but the little seal-maiden had so bewitched him he was afraid that if she found her skin she would leave him for ever.

And so, with the little sealskin safely hidden, he went to the maiden to comfort her. At first she shrank from him in fear, but when she saw he meant no harm, and that she was helpless now without the magic skin, she let him lead her to his boat.

For a day and a night they sailed in the little boat before they reached the harbour of Pomona. The fisherman found his friends already returned from the fishing. They crowded about his boat anxious to know what had befallen him, and he told them of the landfall on the strange island. But he said little of the maiden dressed in the remnants of a sail who accompanied him, except that he had brought her back to wed.

For several years the fisherman and the little seal-maiden lived happily in a humble cottage on the edge of the sea. While he fished or tended his few crops she looked after his home. One day a child was born to them, and the fisherman's happiness was complete. But every year as the Eve of St John approached, the fisherman saw a change come over his seal-wife. Each day when her work was finished and the child asleep she would go down to the sea and listen to the fretting of the waves on the shore. Often she would wait upon the rocks until darkness fell, or until her husband came searching for her. And once when the seals came to play, the fisherman found her weeping bitterly.

When this strange mood was upon her she would wait until her husband had gone, then she would search everywhere for her lost sealskin. But the fisherman had taken care to hide it in the darkest corner of the loft, under a heap of old nets.

One day the fisherman came over the hill to find his little son weeping in the cot, and the fire cold in the hearth. He sought his wife by the shore where she sometimes went to gather the wrack, and across the moor behind the hill. And then he remembered it was midsummer, the Eve of Good Saint John.

He went to the loft, lifted the nets from the corner ; the little tawny sealskin was no longer there. Quickly he made his way to the bay where the seals sometimes came to rest. But before he was half-way the sad voices of the seals were in his ears and his heart was heavy.

At the edge of the bay, where the surf broke upon a great ledge of rock, he saw his wife. She was seated with the sealskin on her lap, and the grey seals were gathered about her feet.

He called to her as he ran, pleading for her to remember the infant she had left in the cot, but his voice was blown back over his shoulder. When he saw her rise and cover herself with the tawny skin he knew that she was lost to him. The seals were already edging from the shore, calling to her to follow. At last with a strand of weed about her hair she slipped into the deep water and vanished.

[*The hero of an almost identical tale told in North Uist married a seal-woman who presented him with a large family. This family founded a clan known to this day as* Clann Mhic Codruim nan rón, ' *the Clan MacCodrum of the seals* '.]

UILLEAM BEAG NAM PRABSHUILEAN
(*Wee Willie Winkie*)

Uilleam beag nam prabshuilean
'Na ruith troimh 'n a bhaile,
Sios an staidhir, suas an staidhir
'Na leine bheag anairt ;
Gnogadh aig na h-uinneagan,
'G eigheach troimh na glasan,
'Tha e ochd uairean
'S a bheil a chlann 'nan leabaidh.

Printed in Great Britain at the Press of the Publishers
Thomas Nelson and Sons Ltd, Edinburgh